REIMAGINING SYSTEMS FOR
A SUSTAINABLE FUTURE

REIMAGINING SYSTEMS FOR A SUSTAINABLE FUTURE

Sade Bamimore

NEW DEGREE PRESS

COPYRIGHT © 2021 SADE BAMIMORE

REIMAGINING SYSTEMS FOR A SUSTAINABLE FUTURE

ISBN
978-1-63676-627-0   *Paperback*
978-1-63676-311-8   *Kindle Ebook*
978-1-63676-312-5   *Digital Ebook*

For my father and my late mother,
who are my strength, hope, and inspiration.

CONTENTS

———

CHAPTER 1

INTRODUCTION: STATE OF THE WORLD

———

JUNE 18, 2018

I stepped out of the plane with no idea what to expect. I was reticent; as someone who grew up in Los Angeles, California, I was used to the fast-paced lifestyle of large cities in the United States. Tarapoto was unlike anywhere I had ever been before.

In the Tarapoto airport, I felt a strong wave of heat that was starkly different from the cold, cloudy winter weather I felt in Lima earlier that day. Outside of the airport, I saw endless rolling green hills. I was completely immersed in nature.

I came to Peru to intern as a part of a certificate program for my undergraduate degree. My new colleague kindly met me at the airport, and we got into an open-air mototaxi.

Our first destination in Tarapoto was a taxi station where we transferred from our mototaxi to a car that would take us from Tarapoto to Moyobamba. As we began our journey,

I did not know this two-hour drive on a windy road was going to be one of the most beautiful and scenic routes I had ever witnessed.

The rolling green hills I had seen from a distance at the airport surrounded us on the car ride. Sunlight embraced the hills, and natural streams and rivers flowed between them. The landscape was vast, truly a sight unseen. As we drove, we encountered the people and communities that sustained and protected nature as nature protected and sustained them.

Just as I thought there were no better sights left, we passed horses grazing in the grassy pastures. Signs posted along the road read, "Protect the Environment," "Care for Nature," and "The Earth is Not Your Trash." The public proclamation to protect nature in this region was incredible to me. I was in absolute awe. This was day one in the Amazon.

AUGUST TO SEPTEMBER 2019

By August 2019, eight months had passed since I left the Peruvian Amazon. During this time, major media outlets released news that the Amazon rainforest was suffering from massive fires due to deforestation. With an upsurge of global attention on the region, the world demanded action. Though the deforestation of the Amazon rainforest was occurring in several South American countries at the time, the news mainly covered Brazil's fires due to their severity.

According to an October 2019 Mongabay article by Sue Branford and Mauricio Torres, in the first nine months of 2019, almost three thousand miles of rainforest were lost, which was an 85 percent increase in deforestation compared to that same time frame in 2018. For reference, that is over 1.4 million US football fields worth of forests gone. According to Brazil's National Institute of Space Research (INPE), deforestation increased by 222 percent in August 2019 compared to August 2018.

This news was all too familiar to me, because the year before, I spent six months researching cases of deforestation and listening to stories from Indigenous Peoples and Local Communities in the Peruvian Amazon who were devastated by deforestation. It had affected their daily lives, their ancestral history, and the land they called home. Reflecting on my experiences in the Peruvian Amazon while listening to the breaking news in 2019, I recalled the day my team visited the Barranquita District.

Massive clouds of smoke spanned the sky, and I asked my colleague what caused these clouds of darkness. My colleague explained to me that the region we were currently standing in was being deforested. I studied deforestation in a classroom setting before, but seeing it before my eyes was shocking. I will never forget that day.

Around the same time in 2019, while I was hearing about deforestation in Brazil, major media outlets released news of a sixteen-year-old from Sweden leading weekly school strikes in the name of the climate crisis. Greta Thunberg, TIME's Person of the Year 2019, sparked a movement voicing the need for climate action and emphasizing its urgency to world leaders. This movement went viral, and millions of people around the world have been moved to act alongside her.

According to Fridays for Future, Greta skipped school and sat outside of the Swedish Parliament with a sign that stated "School Strike for Climate" every school day for the three weeks leading up to the Swedish election in 2018. Through social media, her strikes gained traction, and she influenced others to do the same.

In the following year on September 20, 2019, she inspired four million people to join the Global Climate Strike, which, according to TIME, became the largest climate demonstration in human history. Since she began her climate activism in August 2018, her leadership has led to the creation of a global climate action movement called "Fridays for Future" that includes over fourteen million people who come together and march for climate on Fridays in cities around the world.

THE YEAR 2020

The novel coronavirus struck many parts of the world in early 2020. I particularly remember the months of March through May, a turbulent time in the United States as the country grappled with the rising surge of cases and deaths. There was a collective sense of shock and devastation due to the fatalities and the global economic downturn caused by COVID-19.

The origins of COVID-19 are believed to be zoonotic (Boni et al. 2020). A study published by Stanford University found that "viruses that jump from animals to people, like the one responsible for COVID-19, will likely become more common as people continue to transform natural habitats into agricultural land [. . .] The combination of major environmental change, like deforestation, and poverty can spark the fire of a global pandemic" (Jordan 2020).

This study is not the only publication that shows the link between zoonotic diseases and environmental degradation. Other studies have shown this link for years. For example, an article published in 2012 by *The New York Times* titled, "The Ecology of Disease" describes disease as an environmental issue by stating that, "Sixty percent of emerging infectious diseases that affect humans are zoonotic—they originate in animals, and more than two-thirds of those originate in wildlife." The article goes on to note the correlation between increased cases of malaria and an increase in deforestation because mosquitoes thrive in recently deforested areas.

May 2020 gave rise to another global pandemic that caught the public eye. This pandemic, systemic racism, has infected our society for centuries and there is yet to be a cure. The murders of George Floyd, Breonna Taylor, and Ahmaud Arbery that occurred between February and May 2020 displayed to the world that the virus of systemic racism, and more specifically anti-Blackness, have deeply infected not only the United States but countries around the world. Given the traction this news gained globally, it became a time to lament the racism in the United States and a chance to reflect on the racism existent in other countries.

LOOKING FORWARD
I listed a series of events over the past few years related to the environment, economies, health, and society. These occurrences are not independent of each other. In fact, they are inextricably linked. Seeing how and why they are linked can

be understood through sustainability. Sustainability is a tool to make connections between issues related to the environment, health, societies, and economies. Making connections between these issues is an important part of uprooting unjust systems and creating impactful systemic change.

In this book, I will explain what sustainability is, what it means to take part in sustainability action, and why sustainability needs to be elevated in private and public sectors by sharing stories of current leaders who work in the sustainability profession. These leaders typically have the words *sustainability, corporate responsibility, corporate social responsibility, impact, climate change, environmental, DEI (diversity, equity,* and *inclusion), energy, resilience, justice,* and/or *ESG (environmental, social, governance)* in their professional titles.

My hope is that in reading this book people will gain a deeper awareness of sustainability leadership and also discover how their own ecological self can propel them toward action, servant leadership, and justice. I want people to see this book as an opportunity to engage with systems thinking, escape the bystander effect, pursue equity and justice, and learn alongside sustainability leaders about the importance of elevating sustainability.

My experiences learning about sustainability in different parts of the world have fueled my passion for sustainability and resilience. This book is a way for me to invite others into a conversation, as each step in the process of writing this book was a learning opportunity I was able to write down and share.

CHAPTER 2

WHAT IS SUSTAINABILITY?

———

JUNE 24, 2018

On a temperate Sunday afternoon in Peru, my host sister wanted to show me around Moyobamba to one of her favorite places called Punta de Tahuishco. We left the house and took a mototaxi for a short ride across town. When we arrived at Punta de Tahuishco, I was thrilled to see many vibrant flags decorating the streets in celebration of the Festival of San Juan.

I remember walking past crowds of people as my host sister and I made our way to a scenic lookout, navigating countless steps to the port of a massive river. As we descended to the river, I stopped and took a moment to appreciate the stunning view. Once more, I found myself staring at rolling green hills as far as the eye could see.

As we continued to walk down the steps, I started to see signs that proclaimed the protection of nature. One sign had a message in particular that resonated with me. Translated from

Spanish to English, it read, "The Earth is not an inheritance from our ancestors but a loan from our children."

Why had I not seen more public signs like this in my hometown of Los Angeles or in other cities in the United States? I wondered why there was not more public consensus about our need to protect and care for the Earth, the only home we have. If the signs I saw at Punta de Tahuishco, which simply encouraged the value and protection of nature, were transposed to the States, there would be a risk of politicization or, dare I say it, *controversy*. The fact that cultural context can dictate agreement on caring for the Earth befuddled me.

I was moved by the quote on that sign in Moyobamba because we need this kind of mindset shift from *ownership* and *entitlement* to *conservation*, *protection*, and *responsibility*. This quote flips the narrative that we are in the world to *take*, have *more*, and *toss* when we are done. Instead, it gets us, or it at least got me, to see that perhaps our core purpose is to be stewards of the Earth for the benefit of others and our children.

REFLECTING ON HISTORY

As the term *sustainability* continues to gain traction around the world, understanding what this term was originally intended to represent is critical. First, it is important acknowledge that sustainability as a term is fairly new. One may argue that the practice of sustainability is not new, as many communities around the world have been intentional about living within their means for ages. But the idea of putting a name to the practice of sustainability came about in the twentieth century. The evolution of sustainability as a term came in four waves in 1968, 1972, 1987, and 1994.

In 1968, Garrett Hardin questioned the harmful effects business as usual had on the environment in *The Tragedy of the Commons*, where he "argues that business as usual in regard to natural resources and the environment will lead to a collapse of ecosystems." In 1972, a report commissioned by the Club of Rome called *The Limits to Growth* "focused on the concept of exponential growth in order to demonstrate the quickly increasing nature of environmental problems— including the growth of population and the depletion of natural resources." Similar to what Hardin mentions in *The Tragedy of the Commons*, *The Limits to Growth* discusses the idea that continuing "business as usual" and using resources in excess as our population rapidly increases will limit our capacity to sustain ourselves.

In 1987, the World Commission on Environment and Development (now known as the Brundtland Commission) released *Our Common Future*, and the term *sustainable development* was coined and defined as "development that meets the needs of the present without compromising the ability of future generations to meet their own needs." Understanding the links between the terms *sustainable development* and *sustainability* is important. In the book *Leading Change Toward Sustainability*, Bob Doppelt delineates how sustainability is "the goal" and sustainable development is "the behavior needed to achieve that goal." Therefore, the Brundtland Commission's definition of sustainable development provided the foundation for sustainability as we know the term today.

In 1994, John Elkington coined the phrase "triple bottom line" which defines sustainability as a multidimensional concept composed of three main focus areas: social, environmental, and economic. Another way to describe the triple bottom line is through the well-known alliteration of "people, planet, profit," which was coined by Elkington in 1995. I had the privilege of interviewing John Elkington for this book, and in our conversation, he elaborated on why he formulated the phrase "triple bottom line" and how it became so widespread. I wanted to hear firsthand what sustainability meant before he coined the phrase to understand why he felt the need to expand on the definition of sustainability through the triple bottom line. Here is his story:

> Prior to the triple bottom line, sustainability was largely about what the Business Council for Sustainable Development referred to as "eco-efficiency." With eco-efficiency, the question was how you make or save money by cutting back on waste and dollar use of resources, including energy and so on. There is nothing wrong with that, but it struck me at the time as a rather partial agenda. And so, in 1995, I came up with the "people, planet, profit" formulation.

> If you go back to the Brundtland Commission Report, published in 1987, they were already talking about how social, economic, and environmental factors influenced businesses. So, the triple bottom line was not incredibly novel, but it actually took me and a colleague eighteen months to get to that three-word sentence, and now it has gone endemic.

The triple bottom line united traditionally siloed concepts into a symbiotic relationship that demonstrates how environmental, social, and economic factors are part of an interdependent system. This created a lens for the world to see how it could play a role in holistically uplifting the well-being and flourishing of people and nature.

RETHINKING THE TRIPLE BOTTOM LINE

I first learned about sustainability as the triple bottom line in the fall of 2017 while studying abroad in Copenhagen, Denmark, for a college semester. In my class called Business Strategies in the Transition toward a Sustainable Economy, my professor introduced the concept of the triple bottom line, and I remember being so excited about this idea because it gives businesses purpose beyond solely profit. The triple bottom line challenged the norms of business and included sustainability as an integral part of strategy. The thought that businesses could purposefully commit to prioritizing the well-being of people, profit, *and* the planet excited and intrigued me.

Twenty-four years after its conception in 1994, John Elkington recalled the phrase "triple bottom line" in an article he wrote for the *Harvard Business Review* in 2018. In the article, he wrote:

> Success or failure on sustainability goals cannot be measured only in terms of profit and loss. It must also be measured in terms of the well-being of billions of people and the health of our planet, and the sustainability sector's record in moving the needle on those goals has been decidedly mixed [. . .]. The original idea of the triple bottom line was wider [. . .]

[and meant to encourage] businesses to track and manage economic (not just financial), social, and environmental value added—or destroyed [. . .]. But the triple bottom line wasn't designed to be just an accounting tool. It was supposed to provoke deeper thinking about capitalism and its future, but many early adopters understood the concept as a balancing act, adopting a trade-off mentality. Thousands of TBL [triple bottom line] reports are now produced annually, though it is far from clear that the resulting data are being aggregated and analyzed in ways that genuinely help decision-takers and policy-makers to track, understand, and manage the systemic effects of human activity [. . .]. Clearly, the triple bottom line has failed to bury the single bottom line paradigm [. . .]. [But the] TBL's stated goal from the outset was system change.

Through his article, Elkington raises the point that the triple bottom line has not been utilized the way it was intended. Instead, he argues it has been turned into something that companies have used to simply check a box, perhaps due to external pressure or to remain competitive in the market. The real goal, however, is for companies to truly engage with its three elements—social, environmental, and economic—as a way to create transformative, long-term systemic change.

I asked about the recall during my conversation with Elkington, to which he stated:

The triple bottom line is out there and is doing great work, but I felt we were assuming that because we were thinking in three dimensions, systemic crises would be solved. And I do not think that is remotely true. The recall was designed to ask the question: Are we really, really sure that the triple bottom line, shared value, ESG (environmental, social, and governance), and all of the ideas that spooled out later on from the triple bottom line are really moving us in the right direction and at the right speed? And my answer was no. I have now gone through a two-year process of trying to work out the question: If not that, then what? And the conclusion simply is there is nothing intrinsically wrong with the triple bottom line as long as we think about it in the right way.

For the last twenty-five years, businesses have pursued efficiency (including eco-efficiency). The trouble with efficiency is that it drives out resilience. Resilience is increasingly going to become important in how we design and operate supply chains and business models of national economies. However, the only way you can deliver long-term resilience for the critical systems we depend on—such as communities, economies, and the natural environment—is to regenerate them, since they are all in decline at the moment.

The creation of the triple bottom line was an incredibly powerful and much-needed disruption. It got people to recognize the nexus between economies, civil society, and the biosphere and granted them the opportunity for transparency, purpose, and accountability in an unconventional way.

But Elkington now brings awareness to the idea that the coalescence of the environmental, social, and economic dimensions does not mean we have reached competence. In fact, the coalescence of these dimensions merely scratches the surface. To create lasting impact and withstand disasters, pandemics, and injustices, sustainability and its triple bottom line are just the start. Now, we realize an urgent imperative pushes us to go much deeper, think far beyond these ideas, and seek resilience and regeneration.

Reflecting on its history, sustainability is an extremely dynamic, ever-evolving, new, and contested concept. No one straightforward method can define or measure it. This history is critical for understanding how we as a society are to navigate and elevate sustainability moving forward.

PERSPECTIVES ON ENGAGING SUSTAINABILITY BEYOND THE TRIPLE BOTTOM LINE

In an effort to expand my knowledge of how sustainability is understood, I wanted to hear from other sustainability leaders who have varied outlooks on how to define the concept. I had the opportunity to speak with Hunter Lovins, author of *Natural Capitalism*, and I was intrigued by her statement that "good sustainability follows what [she calls] the *integrated* bottom line, not the triple bottom line." Lovins described to me how the triple bottom line was not encouraging companies to account for environmental and social factors and "in the event that profit is threatened, almost every company [sheds its environmental and social efforts and reverts to] traditional profit maximization." But the integrated bottom line, she stated, is the basis for regenerative value creation because as companies pursue responsible business practices in their operations, long-term value results.

The integrated bottom line, which was a term originally coined by impact investor Theo Ferguson, challenged the way I thought about the triple bottom line on a much deeper level. I had not considered that perhaps the "triple" part of the triple bottom line was still perceiving environmental, social, and economic factors as separate.

The semantic change from "triple" to "integrated" bottom line displays the impact words have on meaning and our understanding of concepts. The use of "integrated" instills a much-needed synergy for these different focus areas. Beyond thinking of environmental, social, and economic factors as three dimensions, perhaps the key to advancing resilience and regeneration is seeing the triple bottom line through its own systems lens, placing emphasis on how the three dimensions are all integrated parts of the same bottom line.

Thus far, I have primarily discussed sustainability as applicable to business, but sustainability as a concept is not limited to companies. Where there is business, there is also policy and government. As I was interviewing sustainability leaders for this book, a former director of sustainability of two global technology companies highlighted this topic for me by noting, "We need solutions that require business and governments to work together. That means companies really need to get out of the mode of thinking of themselves as individual actors [. . .] they need to think much more strategically about how they can play a proactive positive role in the communities and in the regions where they operate."

The former director of sustainability precisely articulates the importance of self-awareness and community awareness. We must have a heightened sense of self-awareness to recognize that working together creates the potential for better results and to understand how one's own activities and operations impact others. Beyond that, public and private sectors must be willing to work together to leverage greater opportunities for long-term impact.

This brings me to the vital discussion on community. When I interviewed a former sustainability coordinator and equity program manager of a local city government who also owns a strategic equity advisory (I refer to her as an "equity leader" in the remainder of this chapter for concision), she powerfully challenged how sustainability is typically understood and reimagined the conventional triple bottom line: "The conversation on sustainability is very much dominated in a market context. The concept of the triple bottom line is defined as 'people, planet, and profit.' That interpretation of sustainability is based on an economy that exploits nature and people. If you are generating profit, exploitation is the inherent outcome. *People, planet, profit* uses sustainability as a new mechanism to affirm existing power dynamics rather than rebalancing. Sustainability is supposed to be about rebalancing, but its current method does not rebalance anything, and I think that is where the frustration comes from in communities. Communities see sustainability policies that have not benefited folks on the front line—folks who are impacted, folks who need it to work. So, I like a different *P.* I like to use the word *prosperity*, which has a different outcome than just *profit*."

The equity leader's statement sheds light on the idea that traditional "good work" may actually be perpetuating unjust, oppressive systems. This awareness is crucial, especially when it comes to sustainability work. In sustainability, it is easy to believe this type of work is always "good work" and our commitment to saving the planet provides us fulfillment in thinking we are making the world a better place. But there is a dire need to reflect on our motivations. Who are we truly doing this work to impact and protect? Perhaps we act out of performativity or some sense of self-righteousness. Or perhaps we really do believe our sole motivation is the desire to protect the planet, but we are overlooking or unaware of the bigger picture that within our planet there are people. If we are not careful, we can fall prey to reinforcing barriers that prevent other people's prosperity.

When I initially thought about the triple bottom line, I did not consider that its essence, which has built the foundation of our concept of sustainability today, does not answer the question of *which* current and future generations we are working to protect. By including profit as part of the definition of sustainability, perhaps we are overlooking the fact that profit inherently oppresses, excludes, and marginalizes people and communities.

I appreciated the equity leader's critique of the triple bottom line, as I think it called for much-needed reflection and reevaluation. Despite this, Elkington's concept of the triple bottom line as *people, planet, profit* should not be discounted entirely. Notably, when Elkington was formulating the triple bottom line, he actively considered *prosperity* instead of *profit*. He ultimately decided on the word *profit* because he wanted the triple bottom line to be relevant to business leaders who were not formerly considering social and environmental impacts in their corporate actions.

Elkington's *people, planet,* and *profit* works within society's paradigm and norms to make a systemic transformation, whereas the equity leader's *people, planet,* and *prosperity* calls for a paradigm shift and works against societal norms to transform them. Neither idea is right or wrong when looking at it solely through a paradigmatic lens: essentially, Elkington's definition is working within the already established system and the equity leader's is working outside the system. When creating a cultural and societal transformation, both strategies are warranted.

The ultimate goal of sustainability is to seek prosperity rather than solely profit. Sustainability is a tool for lasting survival, flourishing, resilience, and regeneration for people and planet, now and in the future. With an understanding that current unjust systems run deep and uprooting them will not be an immediate process, we can still work to change them by speaking the language of those in positions of power—money and profit. Money talks because it historically and presently dominates the lens through which we see the world, or our paradigm. We need to instill change both within current systems and beyond current systems, and I believe together, both Elkington and the equity leader's definitions provide paths toward much-needed systemic transformation.

"JUST SUSTAINABILITIES"
"Just sustainabilities," an entirely distinct concept from the triple bottom line, stems from but also deviates from sustainability as it invokes a new paradigm. The phrase "just sustainabilities" was coined by Julian Agyeman, Robert Bullard, and Bob Evans with the recognition that "sustainability

cannot be simply a 'green' or 'environmental' concern [. . .].
A truly sustainable society is one where wider questions of
social needs and welfare and economic opportunity are inte-
grally related to environmental limits imposed by supporting
ecosystems" (Agyeman et al. 2002).

I interviewed author and graduate school professor Julian
Agyeman to learn about his development of just sustainabilities. He stated:

> We developed the concept of just sustainabilities
> because we realized there was what I call an "equity
> deficit." We really wanted to bring the idea of jus-
> tice from the environmental justice movement into
> this concept of sustainability. I do not like the prefix
> "just"—I wish we could just talk about sustainability
> so people would understand that social justice was
> an integral part of that. But that is not the case. In
> fact, when people talk about sustainability, most
> people are talking about environmental sustainabil-
> ity. If we went out into the streets of your city or my
> city and asked ten people what sustainability was,
> they would say, "It's about the environment, isn't it?"
> Nine out of ten or even ten out of ten people would
> say that, and yes, it is about the environment. But
> I could envisage a green and sustainable world that
> was deeply socially unjust. You only have to look at
> Minneapolis or Portland, for example. These cities
> are becoming more sustainable, with cycling, urban
> parks, all of the good stuff we know about, but they
> just scratch the surface, and they are deeply, deeply
> racially segregated and unequal.

Listening to Agyeman and learning about the inspiration for the development of just sustainabilities was encouraging to say the least. Ever since I began to engage in sustainability work, I noticed something was missing. Sustainability was restricted to environmental matters, and it excluded matters of equity and social justice. This concerned me, since sustainability at its core is meant to protect the future of *both* people and planet.

As I continued my research to deepen my understanding of just sustainabilities, I read an article written by Agyeman titled, "Just Sustainabilities" that defines the phrase as "integrating social needs and welfare [that offer] a more 'just,' rounded, equity-focused definition of sustainability and sustainable development than Brundtland, while not negating the real environmental threats. A 'just' sustainability is therefore: 'The need to ensure a better quality of life for all, now and into the future, in a just and equitable manner, whilst living within the limits of supporting ecosystems' (Agyeman et al. 2003, 5). While defining a 'just sustainability,' we subsequently used the term 'just sustainabilities' because we acknowledged that the singular form suggests there is one prescription, one template, or one model for sustainability that can be universalized. The plural, however, acknowledges the relative, place- and culturally bound nature of the concept."

Just sustainabilities centers equity so that in the pursuit of sustainability, the people who climate change impacts the most are inherently set up to flourish. I was enlightened when I learned why Agyeman chose to make the phrase plural as an acknowledgment that sustainability means many things to many people based on varied cultural contexts. This affirms that no single solution can make the world sustainable and, consequently, there is not one way to define sustainability.

When I interviewed Agyeman, I asked him for examples of cities already living out this concept of just sustainabilities. He gave me an example—one which he talks about in his book *Introducing Just Sustainabilities: Policy, Planning, and Practice*—Curitiba, Brazil. In our conversation, he stated, "In Curitiba, the bus rapid transit system was not built to be green. It was built for equity reasons because the planners in Curitiba realized people who could not afford cars had no access to the city. So they developed a revolutionary transit system, which is still the go-to example for transport engineers and urban planners around the world. The main driver for the development of this rapid transit system was equity, but they had a result that is greener, more just, and more sustainable."

Curitiba serves as an example of hope. It shows us that we *can* do it. We can build a world that does not exclude or marginalize people and that promotes the prosperity of all people *and* the environment. The rapid transit system of Curitiba lives out just sustainabilities and displays that by pursuing equity at the core of our actions, we can pave the way toward a more just, sustainable, and resilient future for all.

CHAPTER 3

IGNORANCE IS BLISS: COMING TO TERMS WITH PSYCHOLOGICAL DISTANCE

———

FALL 2016

During my sophomore year of college, I enrolled in an Introduction to Environmental Science class. This class influenced my understanding of how my day-to-day actions have an impact on communities around the world. For example, early on in the semester, my professor had my class do an exercise through the Global Footprint Network called the Ecological Footprint calculator. The calculator asked a series of questions about lifestyle such as "How often do you drive a car? How often do you carpool? How many hours do you travel by plane a year?" After answering all of the questions, my result said, "If everyone lived like you, we would need 3.1 Earths."

At the time, I felt a slight sense of relief because my consumption was below the total US average, which was five Earths. I also felt a sense of disappointment and shock, learning that my daily habits and consumption required 3.1 Earths. This was a pivotal moment for me to understand how my lifestyle choices affected the environment.

Another way the class helped me understand how my actions affect the environment, for better or for worse, was when my class watched a video about how e-waste from the United States was disposed in the Global South. The disposal of e-waste was an example to me of how something as simple as changing to a new phone and not recycling my old phone could create waste in other places and perpetuate power imbalances between the Global North and the Global South.

Because the impact is felt far away and I do not directly see it, I can easily lose sight of how my actions affect others. But a fundamental step in advancing the sustainability agenda is understanding psychological distance. Psychological distance is "a subjective experience that something is close or far away from the self, here, and now. Psychological distance is thus egocentric: Its reference point is the self, here and now, and the different ways in which an object might be removed from that point—in time, space, social distance, and hypotheticality—constitute different distance dimensions" (Liberman and Trope 2010). Psychological distance creates a mental barrier between us and issues that seem distant because we are far away, because we do not know anyone affected, or because the issue does not have a direct impact on our present reality. It is a common phenomenon in human perception, action, and inaction toward both environmental and social justice issues that creates a barrier for progress.

In the case of climate change, people may not understand the need for urgent action if they believe its effects are not part of their lived experience or if they do not know anyone who has been affected by it. If someone only hears about climate disasters via the media or word of mouth, they may not be moved to care or act as a result of psychological distance.

Psychological distance shows that even if someone has knowledge about an issue, there can still be a gap between their knowledge and their action. Once someone knows about something that can be harmful to a community, how and at what point are they moved to act?

COVID-19 serves as an example. People, companies, and governments acted quickly after seeing the devastating effects of the novel coronavirus. Science was not only the source of knowledge but also a source of guidance and, ultimately, hope. From news networks to social media platforms, politicians to business executives, science played a crucial role in disseminating accurate and reliable information on the coronavirus.

In the early months of the coronavirus pandemic throughout the United States, the public eagerly wanted to hear from scientists and doctors about the newest symptoms and hotspots and the timeline for a vaccine. When COVID-19 tests depicted a surge in cases, governments acted immediately and rolled back on reopening phases. Society was quick to respond to the pandemic because we were all directly affected.

Any sense of psychological distance we may have held on to when the pandemic first began rapidly diminished once we all became aware we were susceptible to the unknown brought on by the coronavirus. COVID-19 taught us that we are capable of acting quickly, we are capable of considering how our own actions affect others' safety, and we are capable of unifying toward a common goal. What if we reacted to climate change in the way we have to COVID-19?

During a World Resources Institute webinar called "Climate Action 2.0: Sparking an Era of Transformational Climate Leadership," panelist and climate justice activist Vanessa Nakate brought up the question: "What if we tracked and published deaths caused by emissions and climate change the way we track and publish deaths caused by COVID-19?"

Like COVID-19, climate change has already led to deaths around the world. Imagine if we proactively worked to create policies, laws, and global action to combat climate change in the way we urgently acted to combat COVID-19. Through COVID-19, society has proven its ability to be resilient and to act purposefully. How can we leverage this capability for climate action?

On bridging the gap between knowledge and action, at the same World Resources Institute webinar I attended, panelist Christiana Figueres, founding partner of Global Optimism and former UNFCCC executive secretary, discussed the concept of enlightened self-interest. Self-interest places emphasis on an individual's needs and wants without regard for the needs and wants of others. Enlightened self-interest is the idea that acting in the interest of others is also to one's own personal benefit. Historically, operating in self-interest has taken precedent.

Much can be said about how enlightened self-interest can inspire climate action. Thus far, I have primarily discussed how collective responsibility should motivate an individual toward climate action. But collective responsibility is not an approach everyone may agree with. Enlightened self-interest may resonate instead.

I interviewed a global climate director of a multinational consumer goods company who shared his view that enlightened self-interest is a key driver for proactive sustainability action. The global climate director raised an important point that having a sense of enlightened self-interest helps us recognize the need for systemic change that then propels us to create solutions and avoid the risk of being left behind. Not reckoning with the problems our world faces today, such as climate change or social injustice, endangers potential long-term success and forgoes our opportunity to have a say in what our future holds.

Enlightened self-interest does not discount the importance of how our psychological distance impedes us from acting on societal and planetary issues, but it acknowledges that based on our individualistic mindsets, framing systemic issues through a lens of self-interest may be a means toward the urgent solutions needed today.

An awareness of psychological distance challenges us to think outside of ourselves and our own worlds, and step into somebody else's. Whether altruism or enlightened self-interest drive the solutions toward a sustainable future—there is a dire need for ubiquitous action.

CHAPTER 4

DEEP DIVE INTO SYSTEMS THINKING

———

JULY 20, 2018

My host sister and I were excited to attend a forum called *"Forum Solidaridad Perú."* The forum was for Indigenous women to convene and discuss issues such as climate change, food security, gender inequities, female empowerment, and access to education. My host sister and I wanted to attend the forum to dialogue with others and listen to discussions as they related to our work and passions.

After a long drive from Moyobamba to Tarapoto and from Tarapoto to Lamas, we arrived as the forum was about to begin. One of the women kindly welcomed us and said (translated from Spanish), "Hurry, put your stuff down, we are about to start the mystic!"

My host sister and I looked at each other and wondered, "What does she mean by mystic?" Neither of us had participated in a mystic before, so we had no idea what to expect, but we were curious and eager to find out.

We put our stuff down as instructed so we would not miss out. We joined the *rest* of the women standing in a circle overlooking a vast landscape of green, hilly countryside. In the middle of our circle was a white blanket, and on top of the blanket lay many different fruits, vegetables, beans, and earth elements.

I stood in confusion but went along with it, excited to find out what we were going to do. In this mystic, each person in the circle chose a fruit, vegetable, bean, or earth element. After each person picked an item, we went around the circle and explained why we chose it and why it was significant or important to us.

I began to understand this mystic was a way to pay the Earth homage before we started the more difficult discussions in the forum about global systemic issues. This was a way to pause and simply be *one* with the Earth. In this moment of admiration, I felt a unifying sense of solace.

The mystic enabled us to stop the busyness of life and reflect on things that brought us joy or nostalgia. Some women talked about how they grew up farming a certain plant, while other women talked about how a specific plant was a staple food in their family and reminded them of community.

I highlight this story from Lamas, Peru, to show there are different ways we as humans engage with and view our relationship with nature. The mystic was a completely new experience for me as someone who grew up in fast-paced urban locales. Paying homage to the Earth that way showed me a whole new perspective on how to view and appreciate nature.

Prior to this, my only perspective on nature was mainly from what I learned in Western academia, which was that nature is a resource, and we can choose different ways to manage it. During the mystic, the women welcomed me to see nature as something we coexist with, something that holds our memories, and something to be respected and stewarded.

Viewing ourselves as coexisting with nature rather than seeing it as a pool of profitable resources trains the mind to think in systems. Thinking systemically is necessary for effective sustainability leadership because it reduces our sense of false separation from nature and prevents us from solely thinking about what nature can do to help us climb our imaginary economic and sociopolitical ladders. It emphasizes coexistence *with* nature and recognizes that, as humans, we are a *part* of nature.

Every breath we take is a marker of our symbiotic relationship with nature. Nature sustains us as we sustain it. Recognizing we cannot survive without nature, and vice versa, warrants our responsibility to steward nature while we inhabit this Earth.

In this chapter, I will discuss systems thinking and its complexities. Systems thinking reminds us we are in coexistence with nature and enables a more comprehensive view of sustainability leadership. Acknowledging the systems we exist in enables sustainability leaders to remember why they do what they do, grounding them in their purpose.

UNDERSTANDING SYSTEMS THINKING
What is a system and why is systems thinking needed for society to move toward a sustainable future? Donella Meadows,

systems thinking pioneer, defines a "system" in her book *Thinking in Systems: A Primer* as:

> A set of things—people, cells, molecules, or [anything]—interconnected in such a way that they produce their own pattern of behavior over time [. . .] Hunger, poverty, environmental degradation, economic instability, unemployment, chronic disease, drug addiction, and war, for example, persist in spite of the analytical ability and technical brilliance that have been directed toward eradicating them. No one deliberately creates those problems, no one wants them to persist, but they persist nonetheless. That is because they are intrinsically systems problems—undesirable behaviors characteristic of the system structures that produce them. They will yield only as we reclaim our intuition, stop casting blame, see the system as the source of its own problems, and find the courage and wisdom to *restructure* it.

To think systemically is to limit thinking in silos. This is difficult to do because of our intrinsic nature, which centers the self. Meadows states it is commonplace to think of ideas in isolation, such as climate change, COVID-19, and racism, for example, and the most natural thing may be to see them as separate and unrelated issues. But to think systemically is to recognize they are all related. I understand systems thinking best by mapping it in two ways: *micro-scale* systems thinking, which has more emphasis on the individual, and *macro-scale* systems thinking, which places emphasis on society at large.

On a micro-scale, systems thinking is to view the self in the system in all that one does. Consciously thinking in systems on a micro-scale does not often occur intuitively, however. For example, if I am walking to a restaurant on a sunny day, I am certainly not thinking about how every step I take and everything I lay my eyes on is part of a dynamic, living system. All I think about is how it is a nice sunny day and how much I look forward to eating food at the restaurant. There is great potential to think systemically in this scenario, however.

First, the mere act of walking is a system—our bodies have many moving parts that keep us alive and mobile. Beyond that, as I breathe during my walk, I am breathing in the oxygen given off by plants and trees kept alive by photosynthesis, which relies on the sun—this is also a system. I enter the restaurant and meet the people I am eating with—friendship is a system—an established norm to meet our social needs and to sustain our mental and emotional well-being. At the restaurant, my friends and I eat food from nature—we are functioning as part of an ecosystem.

This is what I would consider micro-scale, internalized systems thinking: to think systemically in the everyday and the mundane. Systems thinking on a micro-scale is helpful in sustainability leadership because it predicates that sustainability leaders are hyperaware of their surroundings and how their actions impact others, and how others impact them or their area of work.

Steve Schein discusses systems thinking on a micro-scale in the book *A New Psychology for Sustainability Leadership: The Hidden Power of Ecological Worldviews*. In the book, Schein discusses the ecological worldview, the ecological self, action logic, post-conventional worldviews, Kegan's orders of consciousness, and the ways in which these concepts relate to the psychology of sustainability leaders. These concepts are worth exploring to uncover how sustainability leaders wield their complex intellect to consciously place themselves in the system and purposefully act to catalyze sustainable change.

As I explore the concepts from Schein's book, I will connect them with topics in "An Ecological Worldview as Basis for a Regenerative Sustainability Paradigm for the Built Environment," a paper by Chrisna Du Plessis and Peter Brandon, and "The Ecological Self: A Psychological Perspective on Anthropogenic Environmental Change," a paper by Einar Strumse.

In his book *A New Psychology for Sustainability Leadership: The Hidden Power of Ecological Worldviews*, Schein defines ecological worldviews as "deep mental patterns and habitual ways of seeing our relationship to the natural world [. . .]. This includes the way we think about our individual relationship with nature as well as the relationship between human society, technology, and nature [. . .]. Without a deeper understanding of how we human beings interpret the ecological systems within which we all exist, sustainability leadership may achieve only to slow down our unsustainable practices." Acquiring an ecological worldview provides us with an increased awareness of the environment as it relates to society and us as individuals. Without an ecological worldview, our actions, even our so-called sustainability actions, can act in paradox.

The ecological worldview Schein describes in his book is important to consider as part of micro-scale systems thinking because an ecological worldview is the lens through which sustainability leaders view their relationship with nature. In "An Ecological Worldview as Basis for a Regenerative Sustainability Paradigm for the Built Environment," du Plessis and Brandon explain how "'ecological' is an understanding that we are dealing with living systems and all that comes with such systems, including connections, flows, relationships, interdependence, evolution, and consciousness. The ecological worldview sees the world as constantly regenerated through interactions within systems at all scales and levels of existence (physical, intellectual, emotional, social, and spiritual). These interactions result in and from flows of matter, energy, information, and influence, as well as processes of adaptation and self-organization, which in turn allow these systems to evolve. In this world, phenomena do not exist independently but come into being through different types of relationship and the processes they provoke." Ecological worldviews are a way of seeing and understanding how an individual interacts with and relates to dynamic, evolving, and complex systems.

MY EXPERIENCE WITH MICRO-SCALE SYSTEMS THINKING AND THE ECOLOGICAL WORLDVIEW

As Schein interviewed various sustainability leaders in his book to gain an understanding of the stories that shaped their ecological worldviews, he found the primary influences for their ecological worldviews were childhood experiences in nature, environmental education and impactful teachers, witnessing environmental degradation occur in local communities and around the world, or having a sense of spirituality. Childhood experience was also a major inspiration and motivation for the sustainability leaders I interviewed for my book.

In my lifetime, I have had various eco-awakenings that have led to my passion for the environment. One of my most vivid awakenings occurred toward the end of my time living in Peru when my housemate and I were hiking to Laguna 69, which—according to the US Geological Survey, at 4,604 meters above sea level—stood higher than any point in the contiguous United States. I had never felt the way I did on this hike. Every step I took, I was in awe of the beauty surrounding me.

There were flowing waterfalls, snow-capped mountains embraced by the sun, purple wildflowers, grazing animals, calm rivers, crisp air, and at the end of the trail, an electric-blue lagoon. It was ethereal. I was so struck with wonder I had to stop my hike and go on my knees, not because I was tired but because I had to just *be* as nature *was* around me.

In that moment, it felt as though I was in a perfect world, almost like heaven. It was as if nothing could disrupt the ebb and flow of nature even if it tried. It was so peaceful.

As someone who was not particularly interested in hiking while growing up, I never thought nature's presence would ever bring me to my knees. But there I was. This was my most impactful memory that marked the beginning of my ecological worldview.

Through this experience and other impactful moments throughout my life, I began to realize my ecological self. Introduced by Arne Næss, the *ecological self* is the concept in which an individual identifies with nature. The ecological self relates to micro-scale systems thinking because its emphasis is on the individual and how that individual is *part* of nature and all its systems. The concept is rooted in deep ecology, which is expounded upon in Strumse's paper "The Ecological Self: A Psychological Perspective on Anthropogenic Environmental Change" where he states, "This form of identification is the result of a psychological expansion of the sense of self from isolated ego through identification with humankind to identification with the biosphere." This description predicates that the ecological self requires a higher sense of thinking or being, meaning that one is able to transcend their own thoughts, or their own ego, into their surroundings. The ecological self differs from the ecological worldview because the ecological worldview is the lens through which we view our relationship with nature, which can imply the individual is still separate from nature. The ecological self, by contrast, means the individual is part of nature.

Schein explains an eco-psychological understanding of the ecological self in his book:

> The ecological self matures through the recovery and development of our sensory systems, evolved channels for translating the "in here" and the "out there" [. . .] [where] our inner and outer worlds can become less rigid and the mature ecological self perceives its permeability. This involves having a direct experience of the interconnectedness of nature. Ultimately, our empathy for and identity with the broader ecosystem occurs as a result of these changes in perception.

The ecological self connects our inner sense of being to natural systems around us. I appreciated that Schein mentioned empathy, as it reminded me of a common expression, "Proximity leads to empathy." If we place ourselves in nature, then we can empathize with it and all that is embodied within it.

Later in his book, Schein builds on his discussion of the ecological self by stating that "the interdependence of all life remains just a mental concept, without the power to affect our action in the world, unless it takes on some emotional reality. [This is an] important distinction that in order for the ecological self to catalyze a new psychology and ultimately a new way of acting and making decisions, a future sustainability leader will need to feel it."

His revelation argues that leading in sustainability is to *be* rather than to simply *do*; it is not a rote, disconnected task, but instead it is a purpose-driven act bridging both the internal and the external. To be an effective sustainability leader, one must be in harmony with the systems in and around them.

TRANSCENDING THE SELF IN THE SYSTEM: MACRO-SCALE SYSTEMS THINKING

I discussed earlier in this chapter what I consider to be systems thinking on the micro-scale, and now I want to explore macro-scale systems thinking, where societal and institutional structures are taken into consideration. Being aware of larger structures embedded within systems is critical for effective and impactful sustainability leadership because it paves the way for uprooting societal and planetary issues. Thinking in systems on a macro-scale is necessary to proactively catalyze change.

In his book, Schein conducted interviews with sustainability executives and found that:

> Perhaps the most important of the five ways that sustainability leaders expressed ecocentric worldviews is enhanced systems consciousness. This is indicative of their capacity to see a wide range of interdependence not only with the Earth's ecosystems but also internally within their organizations and externally across multiple cultures, ethnicities, and countries. Based on their roles in highly complex and large-scale organizations, these global sustainability executives appear to recognize the interconnectedness of social, economic, and environmental and political forces influencing the sustainability initiatives they champion. In order to navigate the complex global challenges facing us, a strong and highly developed systems consciousness may be the most crucial capacity sustainability leaders of the future must possess.

How are systems established or what makes systems come into existence? Paradigms.

In Donella Meadow's book *Thinking in Systems*, she defines paradigms as:

> The shared idea in the minds of society, the great big unstated assumptions, constitute [a] society's paradigm or deepest-set beliefs about how the world works. These beliefs are unstated because it is unnecessary to state them—everyone already knows them [. . .]. Growth is good. Nature is a stock of resources

to be converted to human purposes. One can "own" land. Those are just a few of the paradigmatic assumptions of our current culture, all of which have utterly dumbfounded other cultures, who thought them not the least bit obvious. Paradigms are the sources of systems. From them, from shared social agreements about the nature of reality, come system goals and information flows [. . .] and everything else about systems.

Existing paradigms have the ability to perpetuate unjust systems, which is why systems change often calls for a paradigm *shift*. In the spring of my senior year, I first learned about paradigms along with normal and post-normal science in my environmental politics class. Normal science is defined as a set of established themes, hypotheses, or methods that operate within a paradigm. Post-normal science is defined as new or novel approaches that operate outside of the paradigm of normal science. Normal science, or preexisting paradigms, is to operate within the norm and within systems that currently exist. Post-normal science is to work against the norm and create a change in the existing system.

This relates to Chapter 2 and my discussion on the triple bottom line (*people, planet,* and *profit*). *People, planet, profit* works within the norm (normal science) while *people, planet,* and *prosperity* and *just sustainabilities* work outside of the normal paradigm and try to change the prevailing paradigm (post-normal science).

The paradigms of normal and post-normal science are two approaches to achieving a sustainable and resilient future.

But the ultimate approach may warrant transcending all of an individual's paradigms. Being able to step out of one's comfort zone, which is the paradigm through which one chooses to navigate and understand the world, can challenge the individual to take an uncharted path to the greatest form of novel change. This requires a great deal of imagination, will, and humility.

In Schein's book, he describes a study by sustainability researcher Katrina Rogers that explores how the concept of the ecological self may or may not influence an executive's ability to act and lead on environmental issues. There is a similarity here between what Schein later describes in his book as Kegan's orders of consciousness and the concept of transcendence and what Strumse discusses through the lens of transpersonal psychology.

The executives in Rogers's study identified specific moments that impacted their outlook on the environment. For some, their outlook came from a one-time epiphany, and for others, it was gradual over time. But all of the executives in the study said the experiences that shaped their ecological worldview permanently impacted the way they approached sustainability leadership, which Schein identifies as "the more advanced end of the ecological selves spectrum." I want to lean into this idea—the advanced end of the ecological selves spectrum— as it evokes a discussion of the advanced mental processes required for a heightened sense of systems awareness, which in turn leads to more effective sustainability leadership.

Kegan's order of consciousness theory stems from a developmental psychology perspective in which the stages of life are outlined in five separate orders. The two highest orders, "the self-authoring mind" and "the self-transforming mind" are where post-conventional worldviews emerge, according to Schein. Post-conventional worldviews are more advanced stages of human development that drive action and enhanced systems thinking. According to Schein, at these stages, there is "a deeper, internal set of convictions that can serve as a set of larger visions or values." Here, an individual begins to transcend the self.

Transcendence is to exist beyond the mind, body, or anything in the physical world. It is to exist beyond the norm. Strumse describes transcendence in terms of existing in the transpersonal, which is "[to acknowledge that] any attempt at improving human conditions must consider global, social, and environmental issues." *Transcendence* in this sense is to be able to overcome one's focus on the self, bridging the gap of psychological distance, and recognizing that the individual exists as part of a dynamic socio-ecological system.

The only caveat with paradigm shifts, transcendence, and systems change is that they take a long time. As systems evolve toward something more just and resilient for all people and the planet, some are still left behind in the process. While we seek to shift paradigms and change systems, we must also think of solutions that do not leave behind people and the planet. Systems change should not be at the cost of anyone's flourishing. This would be paradoxical. In working to create long-term transformation, we must create solutions that attend to short-term needs as well.

CHAPTER 5

INSIGHTS ON SUSTAINABILITY LEADERSHIP: OBSERVATIONS AND THEMES

———

SEPTEMBER 2018

As part of our work to advocate for Indigenous land rights in Peru, my team and I visited various Indigenous communities throughout the region of San Martín, Peru, to understand the challenges these communities were facing.

I recall the journey to one community in particular—with no roads to get there, the only way was to canoe through the vast Huallaga River. We began at the nearest town and canoed for four hours until we finally arrived.

Shortly after our arrival, we began our meeting with the community leaders. In our past trips, the Indigenous communities only had a select few community leaders meet with us. These select few held the title of *apu*, which is similar to the word for "chief" or "head" of the community. This was the first time the apu insisted on the entire community's involvement in our meeting. The community apu told us he decided to include everyone because he did not want any important decisions made or discussions had without the entire community's awareness and participation. This was a vivid example to me that transformation and progress are better had together.

I share this story because making decisions in an equitable, inclusive, and collective way is critical to impactful sustainability leadership. While we may envision and hope for a just, equitable, and inclusive future, we must acknowledge the present glaring fault in our systems due to exclusion and oppression. Sustainability leaders must involve stakeholders, constituents, and communities in decision-making processes if they want to move toward a more just and resilient future for all.

To gain a deeper understanding of what defines sustainability leadership, I interviewed sixty-two sustainability leaders to hear firsthand what they do and to gain insight into what is required to successfully carry out a sustainability agenda. The people I interviewed included chief sustainability officers, chief resilience officers, vice presidents of sustainability, directors of sustainability, directors of corporate social responsibility, sustainability managers, equity and inclusion leads, chief executive officers, specialists, entrepreneurs, professors, critical systems thinkers, justice and equity advocates, founders, and authors.

To gain a broad perspective, the professionals I interviewed span industries in both the public and private sectors. This includes people who work in companies, universities, city governments, federal governments, and nonprofits. The leaders range from those who have been in the sustainability profession for decades to millennials and Gen Z leaders who are the future of the sustainability profession. Interviewing people from such diverse areas of expertise allowed me to gain a comprehensive understanding of what it means to be a sustainability leader.

In the interviews, I asked each person a series of questions about sustainability leadership with a focus on chief sustainability officer roles. I analyzed and reflected on the interviews to search for commonalities and themes across the sixty-two interviews. Analyzing the interviews for their themes allowed me to grasp key learnings from the wealth of experiences the interviewees provided.

As someone whose dream is to become a well-rounded, inclusive, and proactive sustainability and resilience leader, I conducted interviews because I recognize the importance of hearing directly from sustainability leaders about their reflections on the past, challenges of the present, and hopes for the future of their roles. While books and online resources can teach someone about sustainability and sustainability leadership, no other resource can replace the value of speaking with and learning from those who lead in sustainability and resilience.

As I played back the interviews, I identified keywords that embodied a range of themes. I tallied and counted the key terms if they appeared in more than one interview. Then, I analyzed the significance with which the key terms were used in the conversation's context. I consolidated the themes that appeared most commonly among the sixty-two conversations, and, in this chapter, I will highlight the ones I found most pertinent. These themes describe the qualities and characteristics that make up sustainability leaders and the actions they often need to operate successfully in their roles.

Because my questions asked about chief sustainability officer roles, many of the answers from interviewees have the phrase "chief sustainability officer," but the insight is not limited to that role. Their insights apply to other sustainability leadership roles such as directors of sustainability, vice presidents of sustainability, sustainability managers, or even roles that do not have the word "sustainability" in their title but are still purpose-driven roles with missions aligned with sustainability and resilience.

Titles aside, I sought to gain an understanding of the people that lead in sustainability at the highest level in various organizational structures. As a former chief sustainability officer explained to me in an interview, "The definition for the role of a chief sustainability officer is the most senior person or officer in charge of sustainability for a company."

This means not all chief sustainability officers carry that specific title. Their titles may vary from director of sustainability to corporate responsibility manager. Often those who play the role of a chief sustainability officer are leading on sustainability at the highest level in the company, city government, or university, regardless of their title. In some of my descriptions throughout this chapter, I use the phrase *chief sustainability officer* for simplicity, but recognize that this discussion is not limited to that title.

INTERVIEW OBSERVATIONS AND THEMES

The following themes are in no particular order of importance or relevance.

CHANGE MANAGEMENT SPECIALISTS

In my interviews, chief sustainability officers were commonly referred to as *change management specialists*. One sustainability manager of a large city government discussed this theme of change by stating:

> As change management specialists, sustainability leaders are working to evaluate the current set of systems the organization is operating under. They are also working to evaluate opportunities for improvement, such as reducing environmental impact and improving public health and social equity issues. Sustainability leaders work to make an organization more efficient and holistic in all of its decision-making.

> The chief sustainability officer or the sustainability manager, or director or whatever the title may be, usually has to be an expert as a change management agent, an expert at evaluating opportunities, and an expert at building relationships and networks needed to get buy-in for those changes.

This sustainability manager discusses the importance of how sustainability leaders work as change management specialists to evaluate current organizational systems. Change is inextricably linked to systems thinking. Change is a disruption to something that already exists or is established. Therefore, change can be viewed as a disruption to longstanding foundational systems organizations are built upon.

Sustainability in its essence requires systems change because it is not traditional and not mainstream. Sustainability as a skill or profession has not been around for ages like other fields or professions like medicine or law. Deeply embedding sustainability into systems requires significant culture change—whether it is change within the established system sustainability leaders are working in or change that requires a paradigm shift.

What propels someone to seek change or to even recognize change is occurring? I believe humans seek change or identify a change when they understand the culture or system they are in and can identify existing patterns. Whether it is a company, a department, an institution, or a city, these are all functioning parts of preestablished systems that can be transformed by impactful change.

SYSTEMS THINKERS
Because sustainability is inherently interdisciplinary, it requires thinking in systems. Whether one defines sustainability as strictly the triple bottom line, as ESG (environmental, social, governance), or in terms of meeting the needs of current and future generations, these all require thinking beyond one focus area.

A director of sustainability and resilience of a large city government discussed with me the vitality of systems thinking in sustainability leadership roles:

> A sustainability officer or director is interdisciplinary. In their role, it is not just about knowing or being an expert in one area—it is about being an expert in multiple areas.
>
> You have to understand systems thinking in order to understand the various components that contribute to outcomes, and how, for example, retrofitting actually contributes to better public health because it lowers emissions.

This director of sustainability and resilience describes how, as systems thinkers, sustainability leaders should be knowledgeable in multiple areas, also known as generalists. Other interviewees agreed that sustainability leaders should be generalists, while some interviewees offered perspectives that sustainability leaders should be deep technical experts.

A deep technical expert working for a chemical company, for example, might want to have an educational or a professional background in chemistry or chemical engineering to advance the sustainability agenda. A broader interpretation of a sustainability leader with technical expertise would be someone who acquires a deep knowledge of the way a business or bureaucracy runs, by working at a place for many years. This means being fluent at an organizational scale rather than in a particular niche subject.

The generalist may or may not have deep technical expertise in these ways, but they lead the charge in the overall vision casting, strategic direction, and programming of sustainability for an entire entity. Oftentimes, the generalist has a team of technical experts to operationalize sustainability efforts. While sustainability leaders who are deep technical experts might also have a team of technical experts under them who support them in sustainability implementation, the generalist will likely *need* support from a team of deep technical experts.

Whether the sustainability leader is a technical expert or a generalist depends on the industry or type of entity in which they work. Ultimately, sustainability permeates so many different areas within the workplace and will need some form of support and collaboration.

STAYING RELEVANT: THE NEED TO SPEAK SOMEONE ELSE'S LANGUAGE

Another key theme that emerged from the interviews was the ability to figuratively speak someone else's language. That is learning to see problems and solutions from multiple perspectives.

This theme indicates the importance of meeting people where they are and framing sustainability as an opportunity for all, whether from a legal, safety, financial, or human resources perspective, for example. Speaking other people's language was a prevalent theme across my conversations. My interviewees had a strong consensus that this concept is key to remaining relevant as a sustainability leader in an organization.

Maintaining relevance is important when trying to push forward the sustainability agenda because it helps internal stakeholders understand why sustainability matters to them and to others. This brings us back to the concept of psychological distance and how our human nature is to care for or act on something if we know it will affect us now or in the future. Learning to speak someone else's language (figuratively) places a sense of relevance for an individual, which then bridges the gap psychological distance creates.

Empathy comes in here as a key characteristic for impactful sustainability leadership. To advance sustainability, one must not be limited to their own ways of thinking. This calls for stepping into someone else's shoes, considering what pressure another person may be facing and what expectations they are required to meet. This also leads to collaboration and brainstorming opportunities, which can only yield to better and more innovative solutions. Stepping outside of the self in this way takes a great deal of patience, listening, humility, and learning. But the results can be joined forces and a sense of allyship.

When I spoke with a sustainability consultant from a public-sector-focused sustainability consulting organization, he elaborated on this concept of speaking other people's language:

> You cannot force people to do something differently. You need to understand what the actual challenges are that your colleagues elsewhere in the organization are facing and then tailor your solutions, your interventions, or your proposed policies to meet that.

> And that is exactly the same in our role as consultants. Sometimes we are asked by a mayor, "Should I create a sustainability office?" and we need to think about

how to make that case to them in a way that makes the most sense.

With cities, we get the most traction in the sustainability space when we do not talk about the environment, but rather, when we talk about the things that matter for people. Whether that is economic development, work-force development, or public health or safety, those are the kinds of issues that matter for residents and mayors.

As sustainability professionals, when we talk about language, we are really successful in the language of protecting the environment for its own sake, and certain audiences resonate with that. But we get a lot less traction from the decision makers we are trying to influence when we use that language.

MAKING THE BUSINESS CASE

Because we are in a capitalist system, when attempting to lead on sustainability in both the public and private sectors, communicating the business case is vital so that people can see that sustainability adds value.

A global sustainability thought leader and author spoke to this by saying:

> You have to translate all of the benefits from environmental and social to business. That is what the business case does. Lots of us are passionate about sustainability, and that is terrific. But passion does not cut it. You have to earn the right to be at the table

to have these conversations with senior executives in the company. And the way you do that is you articulate the benefits of sustainability in business terms.

A former chief sustainability officer of a large coastal city provides an interesting example of making the business case for one of his city's projects:

> We are adding a fifty-thousand-square-foot addition to city hall, and we are trying to have it certified as a Living Building Challenge building, which means it will be net zero energy, net zero water, and a healthy building for people to work in. That costs about seven percent more up front, but within twenty years, that building is going to pay itself back.
>
> Eventually, we will not have any utility bills for that building. It generates its own power, it collects rainwater for drinking, and the city is going to own that building for at least one hundred years. That is a cash-positive opportunity for the city for eighty years, so it makes sense to spend more money up front rather than owning an inefficient building that is going to cost us a lot more money over the years. It does not make sense to not operate sustainably.

I also interviewed a sustainability thought leader who provides another example where sustainability is seen as an opportunity for innovation that catalyzes business growth:

> At a global software company, the sustainability team reports to the chief technical officer. Their sustainability

team does the normal things that sustainability teams in other companies do, such as sustainability commitments and initiatives to try to increase efficiency, but they also in their mandate have a goal to provide services for their customers. This software company's sustainability team is incentivized to develop services and technologies that could help their customers be more sustainable within their data centers, so they are turning that into product opportunities and innovation.

Based on this example, I think what is needed is to have the chief sustainability officer be part of a team or division where they are not just looked at as a cost center but as a source of potential for new products, new customer bases, and so forth.

One of the main barriers preventing sustainability action in companies, cities, and universities is expense. But it often stops there, with no desire to imagine how sustainability can be an opportunity for growth, long-term value, or business development.

Sustainability leaders must make the business case for sustainability, but, as shown through this software company's example, they also have an opportunity to see sustainability as a means to initiate innovative opportunities for their organization.

LISTENING

Being a keen listener was another theme that emerged in the interviews. When I spoke with a sustainability manager of a large city government, I was able to ask her about what she refers to as a "listening tour":

Similar to relationship building when you are new to a role, going around and meeting different stakeholders and community members allows you to come up with ideas that people want to see happen, and it is also a way to find out other values of the community and your stakeholders. Then, when you are proposing improvements, you can say, "I heard this said in this meeting, and so I think we need to address it."

I appreciated this sustainability manager highlighting the well-known concept of a listening tour. Through a listening tour, leaders can enact circular thinking and learn other people's language (figuratively) to tailor one's own sustainability agenda to what is needed.

The listening tour cultivates trust and builds relationships between sustainability leaders and their stakeholders. This requires a sense of selflessness because it forces the individual to take a step back from their own desires and encourages them to listen carefully to the needs of others. It is a conscious posture of humility and patience. This allows the sustainability leader to deeply know the system they are operating within. It also fosters more inclusive and equitable sustainability action. This focus on listening as a characteristic of an effective sustainability leader excites me because it means the possibilities for sustainability solutions are endless—the learning never stops as stakeholders and their needs change and evolve.

STAKEHOLDER ENGAGEMENT, COLLABORATION, AND TRUST
Engaging stakeholders, being collaborative, and cultivating trust through relationships creates a culture of innovation and

inclusivity. These were all themes that consistently showed up in my interviews.

A director of sustainability of a large coastal city government discussed the importance of engaging stakeholders by stating:

> The sustainability director has to listen and consider perspectives from a wide range of stakeholders. For example, if the sustainability director is thinking about banning natural gas in new construction, they have to think about cost, labor, and workforce changes while also taking into consideration the needs of developers and housing advocates. By banning natural gas in new construction, the sustainability director might be impacting the pipe fitters' union, and there is potential for a loss of jobs.
>
> A challenge for a sustainability director is to not only be willing to listen to all of those voices but to have a trusted relationship with all of them so they get good information and can work together toward an effective solution. Relationship building is key, and underlining relationships is *trust*. Trust is all about being credible, reliable, and being able to connect with people.

Engaging with stakeholders is critical so the sustainability leader ensures they are meeting the needs of everyone to the best of their ability.

A founder and president of a leadership organization describes an example where *not* engaging with stakeholders and not collaborating can risk integrity and the ability to advance the sustainability agenda at all:

> Many times, surprisingly, companies contradict themselves. One side of the company will be talking about sustainability and diversity, equity, inclusion, and the other side of the company will be lobbying and participating in trade associations that are blocking that. It is a huge opportunity for more integrity, more action, and more trust.

Perhaps collaboration and stakeholder engagement can mitigate or even prevent such situations from occurring. Sustainability leaders who engage stakeholders and collaborate create a path for transparency, trust, and alignment so an organization is not working against itself.

INFLUENTIAL

Another theme that arose throughout my interviews was influence. *Influence* in this sense is the ability to inspire people to join in the journey toward a more sustainable future. To influence is to plant a seed of hope in someone so they want to be advocates toward a more just, sustainable, and resilient world. To influence is an incredibly difficult thing to do, especially for a topic like sustainability, which is fairly new and not necessarily a widely recognized term.

One sustainability executive who has led in multinational companies and in a federal office of public administration explains:

Chief sustainability officers have to have a strong understanding and familiarity and empathy for their core business or corporation. Ultimately, they are going to be influencers first and operators second. I used to call this "influence without authority," and this is a soft skill.

Another critical side to it is language—understanding how to translate different functions, objectives, and strategies. Because at the end of the day, if you are going to influence, you have to be fluid in how others are thinking.

This sustainability executive brings up an important point: empathy is a key part of being a successful sustainability leader. By keenly listening to the needs of various constituents and stakeholders and empathizing, a sustainability leader will understand their needs better, and they can incorporate the feedback from external and internal stakeholders into action.

This sustainability executive also mentioned influencing without authority, which is important so others feel empowered to act on sustainability. He also connects influence to the ability to speak other people's language. A critical step in influencing is to make sustainability relevant and understandable to people in a way that makes them motivated to act and knowledgeable about the consequences of inaction.

A sustainability manager of a large city government continues the conversation about influence by stating, "Chief sustainability officers need to create champions in others. The onus cannot just be on their shoulders to accomplish change."

This sustainability manager's statement implies that sustainability leaders need to influence *and* empower people to be sustainability advocates, champions, and leaders in their own right. That is a challenging task because influencing is getting people to think and act differently, but making them champions is encouraging them to lead independently on sustainability. In essence, a core part of being a sustainability leader is to inspire other people to channel the sustainability leader within themselves, which calls for a cultural transformation.

Lastly, the director of sustainability and resilience of a large city government provides a tangible example of what influence can look like:

> In our city, we worked with the human resources department to develop a new employee education program. In this program, every department and division has to nominate one staff member, and we train a total of thirty to forty city-nominated staff through a nine-month curriculum of sustainability education. Once a month, we take this group of thirty to forty people and immerse them in one of our topics of sustainability. Through this, we are building a culture, and we are building advocates across city departments.

I found this director's example to be inspiring for how sustainability leaders can transform a culture and enact systems change through educating others.

THINKING HOLISTICALLY

One challenge of influence is that it calls for a transformation in existing systems. This transformation is why sustainability leaders are also change management specialists; they influence to inspire change by disrupting an existing system.

A former chief sustainability officer of a multinational company speaks to this challenge by stating:

> The biggest difficulty I had was getting people to think more holistically about the challenges of the company. Each of us have our own job function, and we think quite narrowly in that function and not as clearly about how one function relates to another, which then relates to our customers, which then relates to the marketplace. The work I was doing was getting people within the company to recognize that all of that has to have a bigger picture, a more holistic view, and we needed to think outside our own boxes about what sustainability meant to us as a company.

Sustainability is interdisciplinary by nature because it involves many complex dimensions of society. To be a leader in sustainability as a systems thinker is also to be a leader as a holistic thinker and to have an open mind. To inspire in others the desire to become champions and advocates for sustainability will encourage them to think more holistically than they may have been used to—and this is challenging to do. But this is necessary if we want everyone to be sustainability leaders in their own right so we can work together to promote a resilient future for people and planet.

A LACK OF RESOURCES

Another theme that emerged from my conversations was that sustainability leaders do not always have sufficient resources to successfully fulfill their roles. Some sustainability leaders said they lack funding to carry out projects that need to be implemented. For others, a lack of sufficient resources meant a lack of people hired with the skills to support them in their roles. To truly influence an entire organization, sustainability leaders need to be properly resourced and supported. Their work is so critical to the present and future thriving of society and planet that a lack of resources should not be a barrier to progress.

A founding director of the office of sustainability of various prestigious universities discusses this further in the context of the university system:

> Different schools have different levels for which their sustainability leaders are placed within their organizational structure. I think they should all be high level and well-paid, because that is part of the value proposition. If you are just going to stick a sustainability role in facilities alone at an entry-level position, you are not going to transform a university.
>
> If you really want to transform a system, you need to have somebody who is at the decision table and has influence with everyone—from faculty to operators to administrators—to really have an impact and see multiple sides of the challenge at hand.

LEADING RESILIENTLY AND THE IMPORTANCE OF LEADING IN COMMUNITY

Because sustainability is newer in many companies, local governments, and universities, I found through my interviews that oftentimes sustainability leaders do not always feel a sense of belonging at their respective organization.

A former vice president of corporate responsibility at various multinational companies discusses this sentiment in our conversation:

> Oftentimes as a sustainability leader, you are a lone warrior. Many times, you are bringing sustainability to an organization as kind of a foreign concept, and this work only survives if you can build it into the business. So, you have to build resiliency. It is really, really hard work. You have to be prepared not to take no for an answer and to figure out different avenues and ways to get in. Sustainability is too important to not to fight for it and not to stand by your convictions and your values.

Sustainability leaders take a lot of heat, and it can easily wear someone down, especially if the organization is not conducive to their roles in the first place. This means that as a result, sustainability leaders build a unique sense of strength and resilience over time from leading in their positions.

A director of sustainable development with over twenty-one years at a multinational company discusses one of the challenges of being a sustainability leader:

One of the things I do not think I realized is that inside the company, you are viewed as the tree hugger. Even though I ran a business before I went into this role, as the sustainability leader in the company, I was not really viewed as a businessperson.

Outside the company, particularly NGOs will say, "Well, you are in business, right?" So you do not fit in anywhere. That is the reason why it is great to have a peer network with other people in the same kind of role at different companies.

Sustainability leaders may lack a sense of belonging both inside and outside their organization. This director of sustainable development highlights the important role of peer networks. Many of the sustainability leaders I interviewed in both the public and private sectors brought up how they have found it helpful and rewarding to participate in a peer network with other sustainability leaders. Through these peer networks, sustainability leaders are able to share ideas, keep up with the broader field of sustainability, hear about work other leaders are implementing, and be in community with people going through the same challenges they are facing.

WORKING ONESELF OUT OF A JOB VERSUS EVOLVING THE ROLE
The next theme is the one that surprised me the most but also fascinated me. When I asked the sustainability leaders what shape they hope to see their roles take in the future, many of them said they hope the role does not exist anymore, because the goal is to work oneself out of a job. After hearing this, I thought to myself, "Why would anyone want

that?" But in reflecting on their explanations, I think the idea is brilliant.

A former chief sustainability officer of a large city and county shares his perspective:

> When the mayor hired me, he said, "If I hire you, how will I know you will succeed?"
>
> I responded, "You will know because you are going to eliminate my office for the right reasons. My vision is that our sustainability office is going to be out of business because we have driven sustainability so deep into the culture of this government that you do not need us anymore."
>
> Most nonprofits or government agencies do not think that way; they think about growth.

Essentially, this chief sustainability officer's hope for the future is a systems change where sustainability is so deeply embedded into every aspect of society it becomes second nature. This is the paradigm shift we should be moving toward. Imagine a world in which sustainability leaders work so diligently to embed sustainability throughout their organization, city, or university that there is no longer a need for a separate role. Sustainability becomes part of everyone's role.

Other sustainability leaders expressed the idea of keeping the role but evolving it over time based on new needs and demands. A vice president of a sustainability executive network shares this sentiment:

My contention is that yes, things will get embedded, but the job of a chief sustainability officer is to always work yourself *into* a new job with new challenges. For example, based on events in 2020, some companies today are looking at incorporating or infusing sustainability with diversity and inclusion initiatives. That is not something you ever would have thought of ten years ago. But now, companies are looking at that. Whether it is a direct oversight or just an influence, they are looking at that as a part of their sustainability strategy.

This vice president alludes to the important point that sustainability is ever-evolving, and therefore sustainability leadership roles should adapt and evolve too. In fact, sustainability leaders should not work themselves *out* of a job but instead work themselves *into* a new job. This means they must have a heightened awareness of societal and organizational needs to ensure their work reflects that.

When I heard this vice president's perspective, I was enlightened as much as I was when I heard the idea of working oneself out of a job. Both perspectives are important and valid.

But how can one both work themselves *out* of a job and *into* a new job? What these perspectives boil down to is encouraging the individual to be conscious of the system they are in and to reflect on how their roles can best meet the needs of that system in the present and future.

Whichever way a sustainability leader wants to look at it, either perspective will require a transformation, and that takes a lot of grit and persistence. The focus should be to reflect on *why* sustainability leaders do what they do and *how* they are seeking to make a long-term impact that leads to transformation.

A founder and director of the office of sustainability at various prestigious universities shares this thought:

> To me, sustainability leaders are unique thinkers, and we have a value proposition. I hire true systems thinkers. We are multilingual specialists who can work across all fields, and we work across ten areas of impact. You need people like us to look at the system and how the system interacts. And then you need specialists who know their procurement or their energy or their buildings or their transportation. But those folks alone are still going to work in isolation, so you always need a sustainability person to look at how the system is interacting as a whole.

This director highlights the fact that a sustainability leader is always needed as a point person. Some of my interviewees noted that if their roles are eliminated, the sustainability imperative can be forgotten or lost in the system. Having a figurehead may always be necessary, no matter how advanced a company may be on sustainability.

Leaders' perspectives will vary based on the system or context their role is in. For one company, it might be best that the chief sustainability officer works themselves out of a job by embedding sustainability deeply within the organization. In this case, perhaps, the company's CEO or the city's mayor takes the lead on sustainability issues. For another company or city, they may recognize that eliminating a lead sustainability role might push sustainability issues to the back burner, so instead they might decide to keep and evolve the role as new sustainability issues arise alongside current events.

CREATING SYNERGY BETWEEN THE FIELDS OF DIVERSITY, EQUITY, AND INCLUSION AND SUSTAINABILITY

Sustainability professionals are increasingly aware that the topics of justice, equity, diversity, and inclusion are not mutually exclusive from sustainability. There is a push for sustainability to be more inclusive and intersectional. Organizations are responding to this in ways that meet their needs best—whether it is by evolving the role of *chief sustainability officer* to the role of *chief inclusion and sustainability officer*, by strengthening initiatives that combat climate injustice, or by increasing collaboration and partnerships between the organization's sustainability department and justice, equity, diversity, and inclusion department.

I will expand on this theme more in the following chapter.

ELEVATING SUSTAINABILITY TO THE C-SUITE

Elevating sustainability to the C-suite was not a theme that emerged while conducting my interviews, but I was intrigued by it nonetheless.[1] I wanted to find out whether the leaders I spoke to thought that sustainability is more effective at the

---

1   The C-suite contains the highest executive level positions in an organization.

C-suite level or if it is not necessary to successfully implement entity-wide sustainability initiatives.

A sustainability consultant from a public-sector-focused sustainability consulting organization explains:

> It is no coincidence that when you look across the landscape of companies, cities, states, and federal governments that are leading on these issues, there is a sustainability officer with some sort of name in the C-suite as part of the people in overall leadership positions directing that organization. Oftentimes, when you look at cities where sustainability initiatives are lacking, it tends to be when there is a sustainability function that is not in the C-suite.
>
> One of the things we always tell our mayors who want to focus on sustainability is that they need to elevate the position. They need to give it real power and authority. If the person in the role is sitting in the mayor's office and can go out and genuinely speak for the mayor on these issues, they are going to get a lot more traction than if they are the sustainability programs manager sitting in the buildings department or city parks department, for example.
>
> It is the same in a company. When a chief sustainability officer is one of ten people reporting to the CEO, they are able to drive impact and work with their peers to shape the overall business in a different direction. But if they are buried three levels down in a corporate social responsibility role, for example,

they are going to have a much harder time having that kind of impact.

This sustainability consultant effectively communicated the value of having sustainability roles in the C-suite. There is power in titles, including the ability to gain credibility and increase the level of trust stakeholders have in a sustainability leader.

AT ITS CORE

In summary and reflection, I would like to end my insights and observations with this point, given by a former vice president of corporate social responsibility and sustainability at a global fast-food chain:

> The role of the chief sustainability officer is a humble servant role. I think there is likely always going to be a need for it. The role should be an influencer within the company under the radar. It is not all about the chief sustainability officer, and it is not all about the sustainability department, because this siloes sustainability. Sustainability is holistic. It needs to cut across the whole company. Therefore, I think the role should be a humble one that works behind the scenes.

In essence, as this former vice president mentions, it is not about the title, the role, or the reputation gained based on accomplishments. It is about promoting the greater good and sustaining the future of people and the planet. A true sign of an effective sustainability leader is one who becomes a humble servant to those around them.

CHAPTER 6

WHOSE ENVIRONMENT?

———

The history of American environmentalism is generally limited to the perspective of white middle-class male environmental activism. The tendency to view all environmental activism through this lens limits our understanding of how class, race, and gender relations structured environmental experiences and responses over time [. . .]. The environmental movement is a powerful social movement; however, it faces many challenges. Among the most urgent is the need to develop a more inclusive, culturally sensitive, broad-based environmental agenda that will appeal to many people and unite many sectors of the movement. To do this, the movement must reevaluate its relation with industry and the government, reappraise its role and mission, and develop strategies to understand and improve race, class, and gender relations.

–DORCETA TAYLOR

THE YEAR 2020

I was leaving Nigeria, feeling refreshed and reflective after learning more about my heritage, wearing new Senegalese twists, and feeling satisfied from the jollof rice and fried plantain I had just eaten. I sat on the plane patiently awaiting takeoff.

One row over, a white man stood up and cursed:

"You are all animals! All you Yoruba, you Igbo . . . you are animals!"

He yelled it loud and clear to the entire plane.

Prior to this, I was feeling nostalgic and grateful to have been surrounded by the Yoruba language and culture every day. This was only my second time visiting Nigeria, and I was so appreciative to have experienced a glimpse of my father's upbringing. These uplifting feelings and experiences were diminished as soon as I heard this man call me and every other Nigerian on the plane "animals."

This person decided we were all less than human. I immediately thought to myself, "Why did he come to Nigeria if he thinks we are animals?" But I stopped myself, as I could not bear to think of the answer. But I kept wondering.

As I paused my thoughts, a nearby flight attendant, who was a white woman, walked toward the man and said to him, "We are going to need to escort you off the plane."

When the man said, "Why? I didn't do anything!"

The flight attendant said to him, "You are using curse words."

In that moment, I sat pensively in my seat, trying to understand what had just happened, wondering if it was even real.

As I realized that yes, I had just heard those horrible things, I felt a mix of anger, frustration, and defeat. On one hand, this man clearly thought he was superior to Nigerians and had the nerve to call us subhuman. It did not matter to this person that a king was on the flight; to him, we were all animals.

Though I was glad the flight attendant escorted him off the plane in the end, something still did not feel right. As the flight attendant initially walked over to the man, I gained a glimmer of hope that maybe she was going to acknowledge his anti-Blackness and escort him off the plane for that reason mainly, in addition to his cruel language. But my hope was dumbfounded. Whether or not she may have agreed that what he said was racist, she did not bring herself to say it.

Why?

And now the man thinks he was escorted off the plane solely for cursing. He might never realize his anti-Black statement was unacceptable, and now he might keep saying statements like that without any repercussions because he had not been corrected in this instance.

This is one of the countless examples of how systems continue to be unfair and unjust. This is how unhealthy and unsafe imbalances of power persist. Real change does not happen on its own. The worldwide protests in solidarity for Black lives throughout 2020 were held to create change even in the smallest of interactions. Identifying racism is one thing, but directly calling it out (or calling it in) and correcting it when the perfect opportunity arises is another.

In that moment, I felt hopeless. Hopeless because although I did not know many people in my life who would say something like the man on the plane did, I knew that truthfully, many people I know and value would be like the flight attendant, feeling righteous for having said or done the bare minimum but tiptoeing around the real issue and not reckoning with the long, devastating, unjust history of anti-Blackness in front of their eyes. And that thought was scary.

When will change come? Are we *really* in this *together*?

When I graduated from college, I graduated as the first Black woman to earn a bachelor of science degree in environmental science at my college. I did not know that when I committed to environmental science and sustainability, I was also committing to consistently being in spaces where I was either the only Black person or one of the few Black people in the room or department as a whole. I wanted to gain a deeper understanding of why this was, and thinking systemically was the only way that provided me with guidance on the matter. During my brief time in the sustainability field, it had occurred to me that when people saw, thought of, or heard the term "sustainability," the focus was primarily on the environment, and the social aspect was erased or seen as a separate issue.

A former sustainability manager of a global commercial flooring company explains:

> One thing I struggle with is the fact that I know a
> lot of sustainability professionals who are moved
> to tears when assessing the lack of circularity and
> the increase of waste in landfills. Anger is evoked

in talking about environmental matters, but when we witness our Black brothers and sisters killed in the streets and continually discriminated against, there is silence. That bothers me because even though sustainability has primarily an environmental focus, there are people in the environment.

I think sustainability professionals should take that same energy, that same passion, and invest it into social justice, environmental justice, and climate justice.

I felt the same way this sustainability manager described. I often wondered why there is such a noticeable gap in such a passionate field. Our sustainability work is siloed, at least in large part. It only looks at one piece of the puzzle, negating the fact that we cannot truly reach a sustainable and resilient world until everyone feels that current and future generations are protected and well positioned to thrive and flourish.

There is still work to do beyond the environmental side of sustainability. We cannot fairly claim sustainability or resiliency if people are left behind. One way to avoid leaving people behind is to make sure that the people being left behind have a say in creating solutions and in decision-making as we move toward a sustainable future. From my experience, this is not happening either.

As a Black woman, throughout my time in the environmental and sustainability career fields, I often hear the sentiment that Black people are not present because they are not as interested in or passionate about the environment, or they are not applying for the jobs or degree programs where they would focus on the environment.

I often hear statements much like those of ecological scholar Stephen Kellert's in *The Value of Life: Biological Diversity and Human Society*. In it, he poses that:

> Various studies suggest that African Americans evince substantially less interest, concern, and knowledge than European Americans for nature and living [biological] diversity [. . .]. Indeed, ethnic differences may constitute an Achilles heel of the conservation movement, especially hindering its ability to make a convincing case for protecting diminishing natural resources and rediscovering human emotional and intellectual dependence on nature and living [biological] diversity. Until all ethnic groups believe that the chances for leading a richer and more rewarding life depend on a healthy, diverse, and abundant biota, this country may not be able to elicit the commitment necessary to halt the current mass destruction of life on earth.

Kellert's statements insinuate that Black people are, at least in part, to blame for the regression of the environmental movement. I do not feel that his view is conducive to progress.

Others like Kellert place the problem on Black people by saying they do not have an interest in the environment or they prefer to stay away from it.

But this argument lacks self-reflection. Instead of looking inward, the view that Kellert presents incites blame and instills division and othering. This view lacks acknowledgment of marginalization, oppressive systems, and white supremacy. If the argument was seen through this lens that acknowledges history and unjust systems, then perhaps a universal "commitment necessary to halt mass destruction," as Kellert stated, would be our current reality.

Looking at this issue through a lens opposing Kellert's, in "African American Resources for a More Inclusive Liberation Theology," Theodore Walker Jr. writes:

> At one point in United States legal history, a Black [person] was counted as "three-fifths of a [human]." From [a Black person's] perspective, many calls by white persons for an extension of the range of moral concern to include regard for the well-being of plants and animals are morally suspect on account of failure to include adequate regard for the well-being of Black [people] and [people of color]. When those who value the lives of Black humans less than they value the lives of elephants and [. . .] white humans ask us to join them in expressing their newfound concern for the well-being of animals, we are not overly eager to join them [. . .]. Too often what passes for a wider concern inclusive of the environment is in fact a white racially gerrymandered concern that reaches out to include plants and animals while continuing to exclude Black people and [people of color]. These difficulties have yet to be overcome, and they must be overcome if white environmentalists and animal rights activists expect to receive the support of Black people and [people of color].

Walker explains that the environmental movement, which has historically centered on the majority lens, is flawed. It has fallen privy to the exclusion and devaluation of Black people as it seeks to prioritize the needs of the environment without concern for those who inhabit it. His reference that Black people are still viewed as less than human in this scenario resonates with me, as I was called less than human on the plane in Nigeria.

How can we move forward in protecting the planet and its current and future generations if we continue to take steps backward? There is nothing sustainable or resilient in viewing humans as lesser. This does not lead to long-term flourishing and prosperity.

Like Walker's statements, Ayana Johnson's article "I'm a Black Climate Expert. Racism Derails Our Efforts to Save the Planet" discusses this topic:

> Intersection of race and climate doesn't get talked about nearly enough: Black Americans who are *already committed* to working on climate solutions still have to live in America, brutalized by institutions of the state, constantly pummeled with images, words, and actions showing us how many of our fellow citizens do not, in fact, believe that Black lives matter. Climate work is hard and heartbreaking as it is. Many people don't feel the urgency, or balk at the initial cost of transitioning our energy infrastructure, without considering the cost of inaction. Many fail to grasp how dependent humanity is on intact ecosystems. When you throw racism and bigotry in

the mix, it becomes something nearly impossible [. . .]. If we want to successfully address climate change, we need people of color. Not just because pursuing diversity is a good thing to do, and not even because diversity leads to better decision-making and more effective strategies, but because Black people are significantly more concerned about climate change than white people (57 percent vs. 49 percent), and Latinx people are even more concerned (70 percent). To put that in perspective, it means that more than twenty-three million Black Americans already care deeply about the environment and could make a huge contribution to the massive amount of climate work that needs doing.

I concur with Johnson's article, and I think she accurately describes what it feels like in my experience as a Black woman and professional in sustainability. On one hand, there is a constant burden-turned-responsibility for climate action. We desire to act as quickly and efficiently as possible to be part of the solution so fewer people are hurt and less of the planet is damaged in the process as climate change worsens. But on that same hand, it is difficult to consistently bear the brunt of systemic oppression and to constantly face anti-Blackness anywhere and everywhere. Those are two difficult things for one person to face.

Another edge of the issue is that when Black people have been leaders in sustainability and climate change, we are erased, quite literally. Ugandan climate activist Vanessa Nakate was erased by a journalist in a photo where she stood next to white climate activists like Greta Thunberg in 2020. When major news was released of this incident and people around the world were in shock that a photographer would do such a thing, I was not shocked at all. Something similar had happened to me before. Too many are silenced purposefully, and it has been that way throughout history.

An environmental justice advocate mentioned a commonly known adage to me in an interview: "If we are not at the table, then we are on the menu." When people are not given the space to flourish and be part of the solution, then they are prone to being overrun, oppressed, and excluded by the system as it has always been.

Many people like to say that the system we live in is broken, but the system is *not* broken. It was built to favor some people at the expense of other people. The system is working as intended. This is why systemic change is needed if we are to truly be inclusive, equitable, and just.

THE CONVERGENCE OF THE SOCIAL AND NATURAL WORLDS

In thinking about the environment, we must recognize that the imbalances of power and unjust systems pervade the social and the ecological. In her presentation "Beauty and Burden: A Black Eco-Citizenship Remix," Kimberly Ruffin summarizes this by saying, "Both the natural and social world mediate our ecological experience simultaneously." When I picture myself in nature, I do not just think about existing there. I think beyond my pure existence to consider the lens through which I am viewed as both a Black person and as a woman. I must carry the constructs the social world places upon me as

I exist in the natural world, and this can either create in me a love and comfort for nature or elicit a feeling of exclusion and potential danger. This is something to consider when thinking about the environment as a physical space and how people associate with it or experience it. The environment is a symbiotic relationship of the natural and social worlds. As the natural world exists, so does the social world, and all of the pain and joy that comes with that.

Kimberly Ruffin calls the tension between eco-exclusion and love of nature the "beauty and burden paradox." In her book *Black on Earth*, she states, "Incidents of environmental othering exemplify one-half of what I call an ecological paradox for African Americans. I define this as an 'ecological burden-and-beauty paradox,' which pinpoints the dynamic influence of the natural and social order on African American experience and outlook. For instance, an ecological burden is placed on those who are racialized negatively, and [. . .] simultaneously, the experience of ecological beauty results from individual and collective attitudes toward nature that undercut the experience of racism and its related evils."

ACKNOWLEDGING PRIVILEGE IN THE SUSTAINABILITY PROFESSION

I asked many of the sustainability leaders I interviewed what inspired them to devote their careers to sustainability. Many of them said having the opportunity to spend time in nature as a child impacted their desire to pursue this career field. This made sense to me because proximity to nature is critical for crafting an ecological worldview that propels people to be effective and passionate sustainability leaders. But one must consider that growing up exposed to nature is a privilege.

When I interviewed a sustainability specialist of a global audio technology company, she shared her thoughts on this:

> When I was growing up, my parents would not let me go outside because they thought it was too dangerous, and I did not really understand that as a kid. But as I grew up and started to learn about environmental racism and how pollution affects Black and Brown people the most, I was brought back to my childhood and thought about how in the predominantly Latinx and Black community I grew up in, I had no nature available to me or in my neighborhood at all. Nature was completely inaccessible to me.

If a relationship with nature is a common part of what motivates sustainability leaders, then there needs to be more equitable access to nature so everyone has the opportunity to spend that time in nature if they want to and grow a passion for the environment they might be inspired to turn into impact.

The sustainability specialist's example also lends itself to a discussion of eco-gentrification and how cities try to create more green spaces (nature-filled areas) so people in those cities have more convenient access to nature. What often ends up happening in these scenarios is that those new green spaces are more expensive to live near, and that pushes out or displaces lower-income communities and/or predominantly Black and Brown communities. If we are going to try to actively create more access to nature, we must do so consciously and in an equitable manner so that we are not acting in paradox.

Additionally, I talked with a senior sustainability consultant at a sustainability consulting firm about sustainability being a privileged career field:

> It is a newer field, so it lacks stability, definitive career pathing, and is usually not a lucrative career. From my perspective as a first-generation immigrant, stability and financial success are incredibly important in terms of what immigrant families encourage their kids to do so they get a foothold in this country. There is a reason most first-generation kids go into engineering and medicine. They do this to have stable career paths. I think it is good to acknowledge that our ability to choose to work in sustainability comes from a place of privilege. It is our responsibility, not anyone else's, to increase the visibility and accessibility of this career path.

As an emerging professional in the environmental career field, an environmental justice advocate builds on the senior sustainability consultant's statement by saying:

> We see inaccessibility in so many different career fields the same way inaccessibility occurs in the environmental sector—by way of the green ceiling. Dorceta Taylor explains the green ceiling as the ceiling that keeps people of color at only twelve percent to fifteen percent of staff demographics in

the environmental sector. The first barrier is this pipeline that everyone seems to have to go through to enter the environmental career field. That pipeline is very, very narrow.

For many people, especially first-generation folks or people of color or both, it does not make a lot of sense for us, if we do not have a lot of generational wealth, to pursue a career field that takes so long to make sense monetarily. But that is just the reality of a lot of entry-level environmental jobs.

Often people say, "Let's make the recruiting pipeline to enter this career field a small percentage of people of color so we can increase the overall percentage," which does not at all take away the boundaries—that just makes new boundaries. And I think we need to stop creating this binary of who can and cannot be an environmental leader, because it is just going continue to isolate folks because they just renewed different parts of the pipeline, but a pipeline should not exist.

Additionally, as sustainability professionals, we give off a particular aura and portray ourselves in a certain way to people outside our career field. I spoke with the cofounder of a sustainability consulting firm about this, and she provided the example of a time she and her colleague were going to host a panel on anti-racism for sustainability professionals. They invited a nonprofit worker to speak to promote environmental equity and socioeconomic justice.

The person responded in a way the cofounder did not anticipate:

She really grilled us on this event and whether or not she wanted to be a part of it. Her main reaction was "I do not feel like I am a sustainability professional. I do not feel like what I do fits into this space."

I think that is part of the problem with the sustainability profession. People see sustainability as just a corporate environmental profession, not what she is doing at her nonprofit.

But what she is doing is so much of what sustainability should be. She is looking at energy management from an equity lens. That is the goal, and the fact that she herself would not identify as a sustainability professional is the crux of the problem. When she said that, that really struck me because I was thinking, "No, you're exactly what sustainability *should* look like."

Climate change will continue to hit the most vulnerable communities the worst, so how are we building a future that works for those communities?

These last three interview conversations shed light on other entry barriers for people from low-income backgrounds and/ or people of color in the environmental sector. Jobs in the sustainability and environmental sector are often not the most lucrative. This may directly affect someone's ability to work in this career field if they come from a low-income background, an immigrant background, or even anyone who may have a massive amount of loans or financial debt. If they want to plant financially stable roots, the environmental, sustainability, or climate career fields are not always as attractive or realistic if these jobs do not live up to the financial pressure or financial needs people may have.

As I discussed in the last chapter, even sustainability leaders in the highest positions today say their roles or their departments lack proper funding or are not paid well. How can we expect people to take on a job in this field if financial security cannot be met?

As the environmental justice advocate stated, sustainability jobs are often expected to be filled by someone with many years of experience or by someone who can offer some kind of highly technical skill set. This creates a narrow opportunity pipeline that limits the career field's accessibility. Additionally, sustainability professional networks are not building solidarity with communities of color and/or low-income communities, making it difficult to offer support to those trying to make it through these pipelines. The pipelines should not exist if we want to make real change and truly build up an equitable, inclusive, and diverse sustainability sector.

Furthermore, we as sustainability professionals should not portray ourselves as some esoteric career field that only a certain type of person doing a specific type of work can be part of. But this is the way we currently appear to many people. The sustainability field needs *all* of us to create innovative, inclusive solutions, and we must make our career field inviting enough and our work actively equitable so everyone can see themselves doing it too.

When it comes to recruiting, the onus is on people already in these sustainability jobs to open doors to the communities we are trying to recruit. The environmental profession must reflect the communities their work is seeking to impact.

Around the world, vulnerable, under-resourced, and marginalized communities are the most at risk for the effects of climate change. If in our sustainability and climate work we picture who we are trying to protect and then stop to look at our teams, our offices, our classrooms—how do they match up? How is it that people from the communities we are working to protect are not given the opportunity to be represented among us? How can we fairly ensure our solutions are effective or solving what we think they are if we are not hearing from people in those communities? Notably, though, as we seek to achieve this goal in the sustainability profession, we must also put just and equitable systems in place to retain and promote long-term flourishing across our organizations.

A chief sustainability and resilience officer of a large city discusses his experience working to make sustainability work more equitable and just:

> I do not know how comfortable I am as a local government official, or a government official at all, claiming that any of the work I do is quite actually justice work. For example, I do not want to claim that because we are doing an air quality study in a predominantly Black lower-income residential neighborhood, that it is somehow justice. If that community wants to say it is, then great.

But I do not think it is my place as a government employee to claim we are doing justice work because we have inflicted so much historical trauma and are continuing to inflict injustices upon people.

That being said, I do think people are beginning to talk about the differences between structural racism, institutional racism, environmental justice, racial equity, and social equity, as opposed to just thinking about Black and Brown communities from a diversity or an inclusion standpoint. I think the outcomes remain to be seen with some of our projects. But I think we are now much clearer about what a project is and what a project is not, how we are including people in the process, and what those expectations are.

We cannot say we have acted justly or equitably or sustainably until it is just, equitable, and sustainable in the eyes of those who are and have been systemically marginalized and oppressed in the communities we say we are trying to protect. If it is not so, then we have not done the work. I think the best way to do the work right is to include them in the solution. One group of people cannot save the entire planet alone. We all live on this planet, and we all have unique ties to the land and the communities in which we live, so a successful sustainability agenda would take all of us working together.

The risk of further perpetuating the systemic issues we seek to impact is high. As sustainability leaders, we have a responsibility to have a heightened awareness of societal needs to ensure our work reflects that.

A sustainability manager of a packaging company speaks to the systems change needed to make the sustainability profession more inclusive and equitable:

> I think we really have to step back and say that being Black or being a woman or being a trans person is not a barrier. The barriers are the systems we put in place. Racism is the barrier and white supremacy is the barrier, homophobia is the barrier, the patriarchy is a barrier—it is not the person or their identities hindering them from something, it is really the system that all of these years of history and people and policies have put into place.
>
> If we consider that the woman is not the barrier, but sexism is the barrier, then we can think about how we can change policies and change people to be less sexist or patriarchal. We have to look a lot deeper than the people involved and really look at the systems and policies.

CHAPTER 7

HOPE FOR THE FUTURE

—————

What would it mean to reimagine the environment as freedom?
—MALINI RANGANATHAN

FALL 2018

As I listened to stories from various Indigenous communities in the region of San Martín, Peru, I saw how the destruction of nature was also the destruction of systems and people. Deforestation was a recurring theme throughout my time in the Peruvian Amazon, and I became frustrated as I learned how the global demand for palm oil was harming the land and the communities I had come to know. It was difficult for me to see hope, but I admired the people in these communities for their remarkable resilience.

Toward the end of my time in San Martín, I visited an Indigenous community called Shapajilla. Here, I found hope in an unexpected way. Rather than the typical narrative of *defor*estation I had heard about in other communities, there was *re*forestation in this community.

To me, the act of reforestation in this community felt regenerative and restorative for both nature and people. I could feel the joy in this community as the sun kissed the trees that stretched for miles. A beautiful, rustic bridge was the entryway to the community, which was surrounded by hills, butterflies, flowers, and reforested trees. Children played throughout the village while mothers talked about their next business idea. The people of this community were focused on the holistic prosperity and flourishing of current and future generations. The community was full of life.

The reforestation in this community was planted hope.

The joy in Shapajilla was liberating. The presence—rather than the destruction—of nature provided a sense of freedom and fulfillment. In "The Environment as Freedom: A Decolonial Reimagining," Malini Ranganathan states how it is "threats to water, air, food, land, schools, and homes that constrain our individual and collective potential [. . .]. When the land [we] sow crops in is not awash with chemicals, [we] are free. When extreme storms do not destroy the only house [we] will ever own, [we] are free."

The protecting, sustaining, and regenerating of nature supports the prosperity of the people inhabiting it. Sustainability leaders seek to protect the future of the planet and its people. They are collaborators, innovators, and systems thinkers.

I wanted to write this book to bring to light what sustainability leaders do and how they are playing a critical role in the advancement of a resilient future. But sustainability leaders cannot do this alone. We must all strive to create a sustainable future for all people and the planet. To create that kind of just and equitable future, we can work together to think systemically, collaborate, innovate, and be sustainability leaders in our own right.

There is a famous saying by Lilla Watson: "If you have come here to help me, you are wasting your time, but if you have come because your liberation is bound up with mine, then let us work together." If we can see that the protection of nature and uprooting of oppressive power systems create a path to freedom for us, those we love, and the land we are connected to, we will all be capable of coming together and channeling our own sustainability leadership to promote a sustainable and resilient future.

ACKNOWLEDGMENTS

———

My sincere thanks to my family and friends for their support throughout my writing journey. Working on this book meant being more absent than usual in the lives of loved ones. Thank you for being a listening ear when I faced challenges throughout the process. Thank you for your loyalty, your kindness, your patience, and your unwavering encouragement. Special thanks to my father, Samson Bamimore, for being my rock, my guide, and my hero.

I would like to express my gratitude to the people I interviewed for this book. Without you, there would be no book. Each of your stories are a testament to your resilience, your brilliance, your passion, and your ability to lead authentically. Along with the interviewees who have elected to remain anonymous, thank you to the following individuals for graciously giving your time, for providing your expertise, and for trusting me with your stories:

Aaron Schreiber-Stainthorp	Bill Weihl
Aly Khalifa	Bob Langert
Anna Leong	Bob Willard

Caroline Savage

Cecily Joseph

Cheri Chastain

Chris Castro

Cynthia Klein-Banai

Cyrus Wadia

Daniel Zarrilli

Dave Stangis

Dawn Rittenhouse

Dean Kubani

Debbie Raphael

Desiree Williams-Rajee

Elizabeth Doty

Elizabeth Sawin

Gil Friend

Hana Creger

Heather Clancy

Hunter Lovins

Jake Elder

Jane Weber

Jennifer McCracken

Jerome Tinianow

Jerry Lynch

John Davies

John Elkington

Julian Agyeman

Julie Newman

Kamillah Knight

Karen Weigert

Katherine Gajewski

Kumar Jensen

Marcelo Bonta

Maureen Kline

Mike Lizotte

Nathalie Green

Nurit Katz

Rochelle March

Sam Hartsock

Taylor Price

Thomas Lingard

Tom Szaky

Valeree Catangay

. . . and many more!

Thank you to Paige Buxbaum, Cliff Williams, Mollie Freeman, Brittany Pruitt, Hope Wood, and Christi Martin for joyfully and diligently providing your expertise, feedback, and guidance throughout the revision process. You made the writing process all the more collaborative and enriching. Thank you for so graciously giving me your support and encouragement throughout this journey.

Thank you to Kate Pottebaum and Lauren Anderson for providing assistance when I needed support to get across the finish line. Your willingness to help and generously give your time meant the world.

Thank you to Linda Berardelli, Cass Lauer, Eric Koester, Brian Bies, Gjorgji Pejkovski, Zoran Maksimovic, Nikola Tikoski, and the rest of the team at the Creator Institute and New Degree Press, without whom this book would not be possible. Thank you for making my dream of writing a book a reality.

A special thank-you to everyone who preordered a copy of my book and donated to my prelaunch campaign. You made publishing my book possible. Thank you so much for believing in me:

Abby Hancock, Abigail J. Smith, Adeleke Mogaji, Alex Thompson, Alexa Dava, Alexis Shannon, Ali Morrison, Aliza McHugh, Amanda Houston, Amanda Shim, Amanda Wade, Amy Burrows, Amy Sparks, Andrew Peters, Angèle Bubna, Angella Abushedde, Anna Ganser, Anna Horton, Anna Hwa, Anna La Dine, Anne Jekel, Arielle Snyder, Aseye Agamah, Barbara McCullough, Ben Kubacki, Bob Stilger, Brandon Craig, Brittany Pruitt, Camille Frey, Candee Anderson, Carla Jasper, Carmen Flores, Casey Foster, Catherine Wei, Charis Valmores Bootsma,

Charissa Fort, Chiu Sum Yeung (Joyce), Christina Wong, Cliff Williams, Corrie Johnson, Charles Peters, Cristina Guevara, Daisy Astorga Gonzalez, David Mark, Dorothy Mark, Ed Vere, Elim Shanko, Elizabeth Maki, Ella Curry, Emma Beard, Eric Koester, Erin Wessel, Esther Miser, Favor Ezewuzie, Folajimi Fapohunda, Gabidel Miranda, Garrett Pendergraft, George Ojo, Grace Pottebaum, Griffin Walker, Hannah Gibbs, Hannah IsraelMarie, Hannah Westfall, Hayley Anderson, Hope Wood, Ijendu Obah, Is Suiste, Isabella Duenas-Lozada, Jackie Sawyer, Jacquelyn Felcan, Jessica Bubenheim, Jessica Castro, John Mark Daniel, Jorah Griffin, Jordan Perroni, Justin Michelson, Kalena Wong, Karen Babino, Karenna Wade, Karissa Raschke, Kate Pottebaum, Katharine Hodson, Katiana Lee, Katie Boone, Kayla Hurst, Kayley Goertzen, Kimani Francois, Kristen Semple, Laurel Wear, Lauren Anderson, Lauren Tsao-Wu, Layne Maki, Lea Domondon, Lea Phillips, Lindsay Aja, Ling Guo, Liora Hostyk, Liseth Perez, Lukman Dauda, Madison Gulley, Maggie Buford, Maggie Rhee, Marc Hawson, Mark A. Brown, Martin Sommerschuh, Mary Mungai, McKenzie Gallagher, Melissa Bergsneider, Michael Rotimi, Mohammed Abdulkarim, Mollie Freeman, Natasha Brown, Neb Mesfin, Nicole Reppucci, Niko Van Eimeren, Octavia Powell, Olusegun Ajayi, Olusola Oyemade, Patrice Berkley, Rachel Recker, Rhys Webb, Rissa Ho, Robert Mark, Roberta Lanzino, Robinah Mukasa, Rochelle March, Ruth Ellen Bailey Gunter, Sammi Bennett, Samson Bamimore, Sarah Herning, Sarah Holcomb, Sarah Yoon, Sherry Kang, Simona Andreas-Sou, Sinead Mowlds, Sophie Kent, Stefan Jimenez, Suzanne Kimble, Taylor Kirby-Meyer, Taylor Price, Thomas Mogaji, Tramaine Suubi, Valeree Catangay, Veronica Flores, Veronica Goodrum, Yasna Vismale, Zoë Wierenga, and many others who elected to remain anonymous.

APPENDIX

_____

CHAPTER 1

Alter, Charlotte, Suyin Haynes, and Justin Worland. "Person of the Year 2019."
TIME, December 11, 2019.
https://time.com/person-of-the-year-2019-greta-thunberg/.

Berinato, Scott. "That Discomfort You're Feeling Is Grief." *Harvard Business Review*,
March 23, 2020.
https://hbr.org/2020/03/that-discomfort-youre-feeling-is-grief.

Boni, Maciej F., Philippe Lemey, Xiaowei Jiang, Tommy Tsan-Yuk Lam, Blair W.
Perry, Todd A. Castoe, Andrew Rambaut, and David L. Robertson. "Evolutionary
origins of the SARS-CoV-2 sarbecovirus lineage responsible for the COVID-19
pandemic." *Nature Microbiology* 5, (July 2020): 1408–1417.
https://doi.org/10.1038/s41564-020-0771-4.

Branford, Sue, and Mauricio Torres. "As 2019 Amazon Fires Die Down, Brazilian
Deforestation Roars Ahead." *Mongabay*, October 23, 2019.
https://news.mongabay.com/2019/10/as-2019-amazon-fires-die-down-brazilian-
deforestation-roars-ahead/.

Fridays for Future. "What We Do." Accessed December 5, 2020.
https://fridaysforfuture.org/.

Jordan, Rob. "Stanford Researchers Show How Forest Loss Leads to Spread of
Disease." *Stanford News*, April 8, 2020.
https://news.stanford.edu/2020/04/08/understanding-spread-disease-animals-human/.

Robbins, Jim. "The Ecology of Disease." *The New York Times*, July 14, 2012.
https://www.nytimes.com/2012/07/15/sunday-review/the-ecology-of-disease.html.

CHAPTER 2

Agyeman, Julian. "Just Sustainabilities." *Julian Agyeman: Blog.* September 21, 2012.
https://julianagyeman.com/2012/09/21/just-sustainabilities/.

Agyeman, Julian, Robert Bullard, and Bob Evans. "Exploring the Nexus: Bringing
Together Sustainability, Environmental Justice, and Equity." *Space and Polity* 6, no.
1 (2002): 70–90.
https://doi.org/10.1080/13562570220137907.

Doppelt, Bob. *Leading Change toward Sustainability (Second Edition): A Change-
Management Guide for Business, Government, and Civil Society.* Sheffield: Greenleaf
Publishing Limited, 2010.

Dryzek, John S., and David Schlosberg. *Debating the Earth: The Environmental
Politics Reader,* Second Edition. New York: Oxford University Press, 2005.

Elkington, John. "25 Years Ago I Coined the Phrase 'Triple Bottom Line.' Here's
Why It's Time to Rethink It." *Harvard Business Review,* June 25, 2018.
https://hbr.org/2018/06/25-years-ago-i-coined-the-phrase-triple-bottom-line-heres-
why-im-giving-up-on-it.

World Commission on Environment and Development. *Report of the World
Commission on Environment and Development: Our Common Future.* United
Nations, 1987. 41. Accessed December 5, 2020.
https://sustainabledevelopment.un.org/content/documents/5987our-common-
future.pdf.

CHAPTER 3

Global Footprint Network. "What Is Your Ecological Footprint? How Many Planets
Do We Need If Everybody Lives Like You? When Is Your Personal Overshoot Day?"
Footprint Calculator. Accessed December 8, 2020.
https://www.footprintcalculator.org/.

Trope, Yaacov, and Nira Liberman. "Construal-Level Theory of Psychological
Distance." *Psychological Review* 117, no. 2 (2010): 1.
https://doi.org/10.1037/a0018963.

World Resources Institute. "Climate Action 2.0: Sparking an Era of
Transformational Climate Leadership." Climate Program, September 9, 2020.
Accessed September 9, 2020.
https://www.wri.org/events/2020/09/climate-action-20-sparking-era-
transformational-climate.

CHAPTER 4

Du Plessis, Chrisna, and Peter Brandon. "An Ecological Worldview as Basis for a
Regenerative Sustainability Paradigm for the Built Environment." *Journal of Cleaner
Production,* 109 (2015): 53–61.

Meadows, Donella H. *Thinking in Systems: A Primer.* Edited by Diana Wright. White
River Junction: Chelsea Green Publishing Company, 2008.

Schein, Steve. *A New Psychology for Sustainability Leadership: The Hidden Power of Ecological Worldviews*. Sheffield: Greenleaf Publishing Limited, 2015.

Strumse, Einar. "The Ecological Self: A Psychological Perspective on Anthropogenic Environmental Change." *European Journal of Science and Theology* 3, no. 2 (June 2007): 7–12. https://www.researchgate.net/publication/233782231_THE_ECOLOGICAL_ SELF_A_PSYCHOLOGICAL_PERSPECTIVE_ON_ANTHROPOGENIC_ ENVIRONMENTAL_CHANGE.

US Geological Survey. "Elevations and Distances in the United States." Last modified 2001. https://pubs.usgs.gov/gip/Elevations-Distances/elvadist.html#14,000.

CHAPTER 6

Gottlieb, Roger S. 1996. *This Sacred Earth: Religion, Nature, Environment*. Theodore Walker Jr. "African American Resources for a More Inclusive Liberation Theology," page 310–311.

High Meadows Environmental Institute. "Kimberly Ruffin 'Beauty and Burden: A Black Eco-Citizenship Remix'—PEI Conference 030814." April 5, 2013. Video, 48:02. https://www.youtube.com/watch?v=gAX4ptzd9yE.

Johnson, Ayana Elizabeth. "I'm a Black Climate Expert. Racism Derails Our Efforts to Save the Planet." *The Washington Post*, June 3, 2020. https://www.washingtonpost.com/outlook/2020/06/03/im-black-climate-scientist-racism-derails-our-efforts-save-planet/.

Kellert, Stephen R. *The Value of Life: Biological Diversity and Human Society*. Washington, DC: Island Press [for] Shearwater Books, 1996.

Ruffin, Kimberly N. *Black on Earth: African American Ecoliterary Traditions*. Athens: University of Georgia Press, 2010.

Taylor, Dorceta E. "American Environmentalism: The Role of Race, Class, and Gender in Shaping Activism 1820–1995." *Race, Gender & Class* 5, no. 1 (1997): 16–62. http://www.jstor.org/stable/41674848.

CHAPTER 7

Ranganathan, Malini. "The Environment as Freedom: A Decolonial Reimagining." *Social Science Research Council*, June 13, 2017. https://items.ssrc.org/just-environments/the-environment-as-freedom-a-decolonial-reimagining/.